Circumcision
What It Does

by Billy Ray Boyd

Copyright © 1990 by Billy Ray Boyd

Printed in the United States

Library of Congress Catalog Card Number 89-052108
Boyd, Billy Ray
Circumcision: What It Does
ISBN 0-9616792-3-9 6.95

First printing 6,000 July 1990 on recycled paper

TATERHILL PRESS
San Francisco

Order inquiries to C. Olson, Box 5100-CB, Santa Cruz, CA 95063-5100

Contents

I lovingly dedicate this book
to
Marilyn Fayre Milos
who taught me so much

and who does so much
to bring about a kinder, gentler world

and to my mother
who has always done her very best

About the author

Billy Ray Boyd is a circumcised man who lives most of the time in San Francisco, writing and teaching English to refugees and immigrants. With friends, he founded The Victims Speak, a group of "men, friends, and loved ones hurt by circumcision in various ways and degrees" who seek to bring their voice to the circumcision debate through creative nonviolent action. The group also organizes workshops.

Invitation

If this book is of help to you, or if it moves or challenges or inspires or offends you in some way, or if you have additional information or accounts of personal experience that would be of help in future editions, please write and let me know: Billy Ray Boyd, c/o C. Olson, P.O. Box 5100-CB, Santa Cruz, CA 95063-5100.

—Billy Ray Boyd
London, April 1990

Cover illustration adapted with permission from cover of *The Truth Seeker*, July/August 1989, rubbing by Mettey.

Circumcision: What It Does

INTRODUCTION

WE LOVE CHILDREN. Though we often make mistakes, we strive to give them the best we can so they'll be the best they can be. We want them to be healthy and to live in love. We want them to be independent, yet to carry on that which is good and useful in our family and cultural traditions. The last thing most of us would want to do would be to harm our children. Parents who have their baby boys circumcised—as well as others who oppose the practice—generally have the well-being of the children in mind.

My exploration of this subject began unexpectedly a few years ago. I was reading an article on circumcision practices around the world when I became so nauseated I couldn't read on. I didn't know why I felt that way, and at the time I didn't care to find out—the feelings were too intense for me to deal with.

A year or two later, I discovered the National Organization of Circumcision Information Resource Centers (NOCIRC). I wrote to them and read their material. I established a correspondence and later a friendship with its founder and director, a registered nurse with three circumcised sons and an uncircumcised grandson. I began to get in touch with my hidden feelings about my own circumcision, and I learned the medical and cultural history of the practice. Here's just some of what I learned:

◊ Many men circumcised in adulthood report a lessening of sensitivity of the penis soon afterward or starting up to two or three years later. Desensitization is probably greater with infant circumcision, due to the ripping apart of the foreskin and glans (head of penis) prior to the surgery (in adults, they have already naturally separated). In terms of sexual functioning, the decrease in sensitivity often becomes more of a problem with advancing age.

◊ Infants' penises have been lost in the slip of a knife or the neglect of electric current—two in one Georgia hospital in one day in 1985. One baby was subsequently converted into a girl, with the necessity of taking hormones for the rest of his/her life. Botched circumcisions have created, in the words of a past President of the Virginia Urologic Society, "lifetime genital cripples."

◊ Estimates of rate of complications from circumcision vary widely from less than 1/10 of 1% to over 50%, depending in part on the definition of "complication." One in 500 is a figure often cited. Whatever the rate, documented infections and complications have led to impotence, loss of the penis's shaft skin, convulsions, massive brain and kidney damage, quadriplegia, and death. Even circumcisionist Aaron J. Fink, M.D., acknowledges two to three U.S. deaths per year; other estimates range as high as 200.

◊ Done without the consent of the patient, and usually *without anesthesia*, infant circumcision is the most commonly performed surgery in the United States—3,300 a day.

◊ At a cost of $100,000,000 to $200,000,000 a year, 58% of baby boys born in the United States—over a million every year—are currently being circumcised, down from about 90% as recently as the 1960s. Already in the western states, a majority of baby boys are being left intact (uncircumcised). In the future, it's *circumcised* boys and men who will be "different"—as is the case in Europe and most of the world today.

◊ Foreskin restoration—and with it greater sexual pleasure—is possible either through surgery or through gentle stretching of the remaining skin. Both have been practiced for thousands of years.

In the following pages, I discuss these and other facts about circumcision in terms of history, health, religion, economics, politics, parental and infant rights, and sexuality. I address the inter-connected topics of ritual circumcision and anti-Semitism. I explore circumcision not only in medical, historical, and anthropological terms, but, as a circumcised man myself, from a personal perspective as well.

For further information beyond these pages, see the publications listed in Appendix A at the end of this book. *Circumcision: An American Health Fallacy*, by Edward Wallerstein, is the most respected medical work. *Circumcision: What Every Parent Should Know*, by Anne Briggs, and a collection of articles from *Mothering Magazine* are perhaps the most readable general texts, while a special issue of the journal *Humanistic Judaism* addresses Jewish circumcision. Because of its wealth of information on the historical and cultural aspects of circumcision, I have relied fairly heavily on Rosemary Romberg's *Circumcision: The Painful Dilemma*, which I refer to in these pages simply as "Romberg." Unfortunately, it is out of print, though readers can usually obtain copies through inter-library loan programs of local libraries.

WORDS

Several problems of terminology presented themselves in the writing of this book. What follows is an explanation of my terms and—when my usage is not standard—why I chose them.

I use the term "circumcisionist" to mean "pro-circumcision," relating to one who advocates the routine practice of circumcision. "Circumciser" means one who actually performs circumcisions. In the desire to avoid using the negative "anti-" prefix, I have used, instead of "anti-circumcision(ist)," the term "sexual preservationist," or, for short, "preservationist," to refer to a person, organization, policy, etc. in opposition to routine circumcision. To avoid the negative prefix "un-," I have used the term "intact" in place of "uncircumcised," and to refer to the movement against routine circumcision, I have chosen *not* to use the common term, "intact baby movement." Rather, I refer to the "preservationist movement," hoping to emphasize that its goals span the whole of human life, not just infancy, seeking not only to prevent pain to babies or keep them whole, but also to preserve the sexual integrity of post-puberty boys and adult men.

The terminology for talking about the many varieties and degrees of circumcision is perhaps the most problematic. In the narrow sense of the word, to circumcise (literally, "to cut around") means to cut off part or all of the foreskin of a penis, permanently exposing the normally covered glans—or, with females, to surgically remove the clitoral hood. These, however, are only two of a wide variety of things that are done to male and female genitalia in about a fifth of the world's cultures. The term "circumcision" is generally used to refer to all such genital mutilations, which in turn are only one category of a wide variety of bodily mutilations and scarifications that different cultures consider beautiful or which they use to indicate adult status or tribal identity. People in such cultures who aren't physically modified in the prescribed way are often outcast, ridiculed, or denied the full privileges of tribal life, such as sex or marriage.

---

mu·ti·late \ 'myüt-əl-ˌät \ vt [L mutilatus, pp. of mutilare, fr. mutilus mutilated; akin to L muticus docked, Olr mut short] **1 :** to cut off or destroy a functioning part of: CRIPPLE **2 :** to cut up or alter radically so as to make imperfect

---

In facilitating workshops on circumcision, I've discovered that a number of people—especially those who support infant circumcision—initially react negatively and sometimes defensively to the term "genital mutilation," perhaps as you did just now, feeling it to be biased. It's clearly an emotionally loaded term. Why have I chosen to use it?

First of all, it's a term of common usage in anthropological accounts. It's also more accurate than "circumcision" in describing the broad range of what is done to male and female genitals in various cultures. Although the term "genital alteration" would also be accurate, I have not used it. The experience of circumcision is emotionally loaded not only because of people's emotional and cultural attachment to the procedure, but also because it's traumatic for those it's done to. Quite a few adult men feel very strongly—pain, anger, sadness, rage—about having been circumcised against their will (see Appendix E). Since the word "circumcision" has lost any emotional import for most of us—and "genital alteration," while accurate, has a detached, clinical feel to it—I feel I would be trivializing those feelings if I were to avoid the term "genital mutilation." It's a term which is not only scientifically accurate but also honors the feelings of those who feel they are victims of circumcision. I use it to mean any alteration or removal of human genitals or any of their parts. Bowing to popular usage, I also sometimes use the term "circumcision" in this broader sense, while at other times I use it to mean more specifically male foreskin removal. I have tried to make sure that in each case the context makes clear which meaning is intended.

Though there are very intriguing theories about sado-masochistic factors in the practice of circumcision, my approach is generally to assume positive personal motivations. Otherwise, the debate can degenerate quickly into a name-calling contest.

Seeking to avoid gender bias, I have used "he," "him," etc., only when referring specifically to males. When I refer to a singular person whose gender is unknown or is not specific, I use "they," "them," "their," as in, "If someone calls while I'm out, ask them to call again in an hour." Such use has a long history among all social classes as well as widespread current usage. It has survived attempts of male grammarians last century to convince us that—and this really was their argument—just as women are naturally subservient to men, the feminine gender is included in the all-embracing masculine.

I generally use the adjective "ritual" for what is usually called "religious" circumcision. I do so to emphasize that Jewish, Moslem, and other religious circumcision and religion itself are cultural phenomena. In doing so, I am not implying that ritual is something retrograde or "uncivilized." Our lives are structured and can be greatly enriched (as well as limited) by rituals.

The term "fundamentalist" can have two very different meanings. It can mean finding and living by the essential fundamentals of a belief system (truth, love, compassion) or it can refer to a "literalist" acceptance of some (usually written) religious authority (for Protestant Christians, the Bible; for Jews, primarily the Talmud and other rabbinic commentaries on the Old Testament) as infallible and not subject to interpretation in light of changing social and historical conditions. In this book I use the term in the latter sense, in which Christian and Islamic fundamentalism and Jewish orthodoxy share much in common, along with political fundamentalists of the right and left who follow unquestioningly their party lines.

I use the term "spiritual" and "spirituality" to refer to personal experience of, and inquiry into, the nature of self and life, and "religious" and "religion" to refer to a set of more-or-less fixed beliefs, dogmas, and/or rituals.

Due to limitations of text, I've restricted discussion of religious circumcision mostly to Judaism, which seems more culturally relevant in the United States in terms of both population and cultural influence (Jewish circumcision provided the model for medical circumcision as we know it). Some of the points made refer equally well to Islamic (or other socio-religious) circumcision, others not.

The three sections of the book—"Medicine and Culture, Pleasure and Pain"; "Religion and Spirituality"; and "Personal Change and Political Action"—are somewhat arbitrary. Because the various aspects of circumcision are so interrelated, it is impossible to separate them into neat categories. So you will find in each section something of the others. Even the headings are not as distinct as they might appear: medicine operates within a cultural context, religion is a cultural phenomenon and deals with pleasure and pain, spirituality involves personal change, political action impacts on culture, and so on.

You will find that from time to time I interject my own experience, feelings, and thoughts. I do this because it seems to me important to address the issue on both an objective and a personal level.

APPRECIATION

I am indebted to a number of people for encouragement, support, information, and feedback on the manuscript. Among them are Paulann Sternberg, Clay Olson, Arla Ertz, Ed Duvin, Rosemary Romberg, Gurcharan Singh van Tijn, John Erickson, and Marti Kheel. Others preferred not to be mentioned here.

To those in the nonviolent direct action movements for peace, justice, and planetary survival I am grateful for approaches to culture and liberation useful in dealing with the interconnected issues of religious circumcision and anti-Semitism.

Thanks to Shaun, Caroline, and Emma for making room to shelter me during the writing.

Medicine and Culture, Pleasure and Pain

IN THE BEGINNING

The maltreatment of children has existed since recorded time, and has taken many forms....Children were mutilated for a variety of reasons. Circumcision, foot and head binding, and castration were all accepted at various times in history.

—Norman S. Ellerstein, M.D.
Child Abuse and Neglect: A Medical Reference[1]

Various theories have been put forth about how male or female circumcision began in various cultures. In some cases it may have been a way to squelch divisiveness in a tribe or to clearly establish power over subjects by forcing them to yield up their children for genital mutilation, or it may have been a humane reform from a previous practice of child sacrifice. Freudian psychologists used to maintain that it developed in tribes in which older dominant males mated with multiple younger females and used the threat of genital mutilations of younger men to keep the competition in line, resulting in the famous "castration complex" among the males; this theory is not currently in favor. Some claim that circumcision was a perceived medical necessity for desert nomads with little water to keep clean. Circumcision may have been a way of branding slaves, and some have argued that it was influenced by women wishing that men, too, would bleed like them. It may have developed from (or along with) the subjugation and captive breeding of nonhuman animals, with its psychology of domination and practice of biological manipulation (including castration).

The theory which best fits into my understanding of how people and cultures work, a theory which has a considerable amount of anthropological evidence in support, is that circumcision began as a rite of passage, a puberty rite, out of boys' and men's envy of girls' dramatic initiation into adulthood through menstruation and childbearing, and that it changed from an adolescent to an infant procedure with the development of monotheism (single-god religion). Indeed, in almost all cultures in which it is practiced today, circumcision is still a puberty or marriage rite performed on adolescents. It apparently occurs only in societies which are patriarchal (male-dominated), though in a minority of them. In every society which circumcises females, male circumcision apparently came first—though, again, not every culture which practices male circumcision practices its (usually more severe) female counterpart. (A discussion of female circumcision follows later in this book, and a victim's account may be found in Appendix C.)

As in much of human behavior, there were various reasons for the development of genital mutilations, varying from culture to culture. One thing is clear—circumcision came about for cultural and psychological reasons, *not* medical ones. This needs to be borne in mind in the current medical debate.

HEALTH AND DISEASE

It wasn't until the last century that circumcision as we know it started to be done for a supposedly *medical* reason: to discourage masturbation, thought by some doctors to cause a long list of problems from asthma to insanity (as well as alcoholism, epilepsy, enuresis, hernia, gout, rectal prolapse, rheumatism, headaches, curvature of the spine, hip disease, hydrocephalus, and kidney disease, to name just a few). It did reduce the sensitivity of the penis and take quite a bit of the fun out of masturbation, but it eventually became apparent that circumcised men were wheezing and going crazy at the same rates as intact men and that even cutting off the penis's only moving part would not stop masturbation. As a result, doctors gradually stopped doing circumcisions *for this reason*. But instead of stopping the practice, they came up with new medical "reasons," each replaced by another as soon as it became discredited—cervical cancer, cancer of the penis, and so on.

There is no shortage of examples of "knife-happy" doctors past and present—we only need to look at the excessive number of unnecessary surgeries such as caesarean deliveries. But while previous medical practices like blood-letting and routine tonsillectomy have been dropped, circumcision, once established, has proved more resistant to being discontinued. Why this is so is a matter of opinion. Some say it's because this operation deals with the genitals, and therefore sexuality, and that we're less open to reconsidering a well-established sex-related practice. Others say that doctors don't want to admit they've been doing something horrible to so many babies, or that they don't want to lose the quick money they make from this operation. In actuality, it depends on the doctor—some sincerely believe what they're doing is right, others very openly say they're in it for the money, and yet others are afraid that if they don't do it at parents' request, they'll lose patients to other doctors.

A modern-day example of the medical profession's attachment to circumcision came in 1987, when the California Medical Association declared—in a resolution adopted *against the advice of their own Scientific Board*—that circumcision is an "effective public health measure." As we look in the following pages at some of the medical and non-medical reasons given for circumcision, we will see a common theme emerge: our cultural bias in favor of the procedure causes us repeatedly to misinterpret data on circumcision and to leap prematurely to false conclusions. We seem to need to find a reason to justify something we're already in the habit of doing.

Only the English-speaking countries ever adopted circumcision for supposedly medical reasons, and in recent decades the medical professions in Britain, Australia, and New Zealand—everywhere except in the United States—have led the move *away* from it. According to the National Organization of Circumcision Information Resource Centers, the circumcision rates in those countries are now down to around 1%, 18%, and 2%, respectively.

In the early editions of his book *Baby and Child Care*, Benjamin Spock, M.D., recommended infant circumcision. In more recent editions he has changed his stand considerably, and in the April 1989 issue of *Redbook* magazine, in an article titled "Circumcision—It's *Not* Necessary," he states:

> My own preference, if I had the good fortune to have another son, would be to leave his little penis alone.

Nationally syndicated radio and TV medical advisor Dean Edell, M.D., also counsels viewers from time to time against circumcision. Unfortunately, not all doctors have gotten the message. The result is that the United States is now the *only* country in the world (and Canada to a lesser extent) where non-religious circumcision is still widespread. Though circumcision is essentially a cultural phenomenon, the modern reasons given for it are largely medical. Because of this, it is necessary to deal briefly with the circumcisionists' main medical arguments before going on to the more relevant cultural and psychological aspects. Circumcision has been done in the honest belief that it somehow prevented not only masturbation but also cervical cancer, prostate cancer, urinary tract infections, penile cancer, phimosis, and now AIDS. (See Appendix A for books that discuss other conditions which at various times have been used to justify circumcision.)

Cervical cancer. The idea that circumcision prevents cervical cancer came into being when it was noted that Jewish women had substantially lower incidences of cervical cancer than did gentile women. Since circumcision in the non-Jewish population was not common and since Jewish men were almost all circumcised, it was assumed that somehow the presence of a foreskin caused cervical cancer (or harbored something that did) and, conversely, that circumcision prevented it.

Now that the overwhelming majority of U.S. males are circumcised, we can compare cervical cancer rates with Europe, where circumcision is rare. There is no significant difference, indicating that cancer of the cervix has nothing to do with the male partner's circumcision status. So why the difference between Jews and non-Jews? There are a number of speculations. Since the incidence of cervical cancer may well be related to personal hygiene, some have suggested that a traditional Jewish emphasis on cleanliness is responsible. Others suspect genetic factors. At any rate, few doctors these days take seriously the idea that cutting off a baby boy's foreskin will help prevent cervical cancer in his future wife or sexual partners. Most would agree with the American Academy of Pediatrics' statement that

> Neonatal circumcision is unproven as a means of reducing... carcinoma of the cervix in marital partners...[2]

Prostate cancer. This form of cancer is a fairly common cause of death among men in the United States. Again, from observing the lower incidence of the disease among Jewish men than among the then largely intact U.S. population, many doctors concluded that circumcision could prevent prostate cancer. We now know that among non-Jews, there is no significant difference in rates of prostate cancer between circumcised and intact men, and some countries where circumcision is very uncommon have very low rates of prostate cancer. Again, to quote the American Academy of Pediatrics,

> There is presently no convincing scientific evidence to substantiate the assertion that circumcision reduces the eventual incidence of cancer to the prostate.[3]

Urinary tract infections (UTI). According to a well-publicized study done in military hospitals by Dr. T.E. Wiswell, UTIs occur in about one in every hundred intact boys, compared with one in every thousand circumcised boys. "So we should circumcise boys for their own good," we might say—as Dr. Wiswell says.

However, not only were there methodological problems in the Wiswell study (relating primarily to the inconsistent way urine samples were obtained), but now a group of doctors from the pediatrics departments of five different Swedish hospitals, writing in the British medical journal *The Lancet*,[4] suggest that any increase in the incidence of UTI among intact babies is due to the hospital birthing environment, not the foreskin. In natural birth, it's not uncommon for a woman's bowels to move during birthing. Thus the area under the baby's foreskin often becomes colonized with the mother's fecal bacteria, to which the child has developed an immunity. In the more controlled and supposedly sterile births in hospital, this colonization is less likely to occur. Instead, it remains free of bacteria—but only for a short time. Nature abhors a vacuum, and so the under-foreskin area very soon becomes colonized with harmful organisms such as hostile strains of *E Coli* floating around the maternity ward, bacteria to which the baby has not developed an immunity. Once these bacteria set up permanent housekeeping under the foreskin, it's easier for them to make their way up the urinary tract. UTI and kidney infections can result in a small minority of cases (1%, according to Wiswell). The theory is that circumcision, by removing the foreskin and drying up the glans, can reduce the chances of these organisms establishing themselves and getting in the urinary tract.

According to these Swedish doctors, circumcision is *at best* a surgical preventive measure for a low-incidence condition easily treated by less drastic measures and created by hospitals in the first place. They recommend that, just after birth, the under-foreskin area be deliberately colonized with the mother's intestinal bacteria to prevent UTI. This would certainly be far less drastic than amputation of a functioning, highly sensitive organ like the foreskin, an organ far better understood and appreciated in Sweden, and in Europe generally (where circumcision is rare), than in the United States. (The importance of the foreskin is discussed later in this book.) Rooming in or home births would also address this problem.

Still, even if Wiswell is correct, and even if circumcision reduces UTI from 1% to 1/10 of 1%, on reflection we have to ask, "So what?" There is no other medical condition for which a highly sensitive, functioning body part (such as the foreskin) is cut off to prevent such a low risk (1%) of future problems that, when they occur, can be treated with far less drastic measures, as is the case with UTI. Few would support cutting off part of little girls' genitals if it would reduce the incidence of UTI. Clearly our cultural bias is at work when we use such studies to support routine infant male circumcision.

All the hullabaloo over UTI may well be moot. Dr. Wislell's results have been challenged, primarily on the basis of inconsistency in taking urine samples, often by means which leave the samples open to contamination from other sources in the hospitals. This would result in many false positives in the tests. Dr. Marin Altschul has been doing a similar study at Kaiser-Permanente Hospitals. His soon-to-be-published study

...found not a single confirmed case of UTI in a normal male infant. All of the confirmed cases occurred in infants who had clear-cut urinary birth defects."[5]

Another physician, in a recent letter to the editor of a medical journal, after describing the various problems he deals with caused by circumcision, some requiring further surgery, goes on to say that

It has been my custom for the last 15 years to do a routine urinalysis in newborns at 2 months of age. Rarely is any abnormality found. In 15 years I have admitted only three infants to a hospital with illness of the urinary tract: two girls with hydronephrosis and a circumcised male with UTI.

....My experience reinforces the practice of discouraging routine circumcision, a cause of more morbidity than benefit.[6]

So why did Dr. Wiswell get different results? Relating back to the colonization of the under-foreskin area with either friendly or hostile bacteria, Romberg points out that, although rooming-in status of the patients was apparently not recorded,

Kaiser hospitals (from which Altschul got his figures) commonly offer rooming in. Military hospitals (source of the Wiswell studies) frequently do not.[7]

As the medical debate continues, one thing is clear: our pro-circumcision cultural bias causes us (including our media) to give less credence to studies and arguments against circumcision than those for.

Penile cancer (cancer of the penis) is a rare disease—around 1 in 100,000 in industrialized countries, 1 in 20,000 or 30,000 elsewhere, according to sources cited by Romberg. When it does occur in the United States, it's usually in an intact man. The fear, of course, is that if our sons aren't circumcised they'll lose their penises to cancer. Yet the rare case of penile cancer can usually be treated with partial or complete circumcision if the cancer is inside the foreskin, or with local radiation therapy if on the glans. In extremely rare cases requiring partial amputation of the penis, plastic reconstructive surgery can restore sexual function, something not possible many years ago. All of these medical procedures, of course, are performed under general anesthesia, whereas infant circumcision is performed without it, since general anesthesia is risky to use with babies and is reserved for more serious and necessary types of surgery. (Even local anesthetic, if injected, is very painful in itself, has some risks, and is not notably effective. Spray anesthetics are even less effective.)

Because the chances of serious complications from circumcision are 1 in 500 or 1000 and because penile cancer is so rare,

> [T]here are more deaths each year from circumcision than from cancer of the penis.
>
> —Sydney Gellis, M.D.
> *American Journal of Diseases in Childhood*[8]

Hygiene, not surprisingly, seems to be as crucial to genital as to overall health—if you don't keep the penis clean, you're more likely to develop a problem. And, as with UTI (though penile cancer is far, far more rare than UTI), with the chances of occurrence so small, even if it could be proven that a foreskin predisposes one slightly to this rare disease, that's hardly a reason to circumcise as a preventive measure. To put the matter more in perspective, we need only note that more cancer could be prevented by routine mastectomy (breast removal) than by routine circumcision, yet to my knowledge no one is suggesting routine mastectomy of little girls. Again, it is our cultural bias in favor of circumcision that keeps us from seeing how illogical are the "reasons" we give for doing it to healthy baby boys.

After reviewing the various studies on penile cancer, Romberg sums up the evidence in this way:

> The choice of prevention of penile cancer is *either* to cut the foreskin off, *or* wash it.[9]

Phimosis is the inability to retract (slip back) the adult or later-childhood foreskin because of a too-tight and inelastic foreskin. Any problem resembling phimosis usually results in a complete circumcision from American doctors.

It's perfectly normal for the foreskin to adhere to the glans for the first few years of life, and in some cases into the teens. Many well-meaning but uninformed doctors view this normal condition as phimosis and forcefully retract the foreskin or instruct parents to forcefully retract it, tearing the foreskin from the glans and leaving the separated skin tissues to grow back together. The more often this is done, the more likely that adhering lesions will develop, a condition sometimes called acquired phimosis. So what's the alternative to retracting the foreskin for cleaning? Here's how one physician put it:

> One may wash the entire organ [of a child] without attempting to pull back or clean the foreskin. The American Academy of Pediatrics' 1984 brochure on "Care of the Uncircumcised Penis" is good advice to all parents, to all nurses, doctors, and health-care workers. Leave it alone! Let the newborn male take care of his own foreskin when he is able to do it without any trauma or pain. Leave the penis of the newborn infant alone.[10]

A boy's foreskin should never be forcefully or prematurely retracted and any doctor who tries to do so should be stopped and, if persistent, reported to his or her medical society.

A too-tight foreskin can in most cases be remedied by gentle stretching with warm water and creams (soap can cause irritation). In some cases, a relatively simple surgical slitting of the foreskin—not cutting it off—may be necessary. In rare cases, the tip of an inelastic foreskin may need to be removed— but a full circumcision is almost never necessary. Most American doctors, never having had a foreskin themselves and not having been trained in proper care and treatment of the intact penis, don't know what else to do with a too-tight foreskin other than to cut it off.

THE CHALICE OR THE BLADE?—SAFER SEX VS. THE KNIFE

AIDS is the latest scare in the sad parade of reasons given for circumcising baby boys, with an African study of men who visited prostitutes in Kenya reportedly showing a higher contagion rate among intact men than among circumcised ones. There are many unanswered questions and cultural variables involved: for example, what was the circumcision status of the female prostitutes in the study, and what relationship might that have to contagion? (A number of African cultures practice female circumcision.) And why is AIDS in Africa, unlike in the West, occurring primarily in the heterosexual population? What are the differences in the strains of the AIDS virus in Africa compared with those prevalent here? Until studies without these complications of cultural differences are done on populations in the United States (where most men are circumcised and AIDS is widespread) and Europe (where most men are intact and AIDS, though a serious problem, is less epidemic), we must reserve judgement about such claims.

During vaginal or anal intercourse, an intact penis can slip gently in and out of its own foreskin, whereas a circumcised one creates more friction and therefore more chance of creating minute tears in the delicate skin. But even if circumcision could be shown to reduce (not eliminate) the chances of infection, we would still be left with the question: Isn't it be better to teach a boy to practice safer sex than to cut off part of his penis when he's a baby? That way, the future option for full sexual pleasure with a safe mate remains. With circumcision, it's gone forever.

(Of course, sexual pleasure involves our whole bodies, not just our penises; in fact, our primary sex organs are the mind and the heart. In lovemaking, localized sensation from the penis is only part of the overall energy flow. Still, penile sensations for the male and corresponding clitoral ones for the female are an important part of sex, and anything that unnecessarily compromises them detracts from our sexual experience.)

It's been said that anyone trying to protect himself from AIDS with a circumcision instead of a condom* needs to have more than his blood examined. And since both circumcision and condoms reduce sexual sensitivity, wearing a condom on a circumcised penis has been compared to wearing two on an intact one. So routine circumcision may actually have helped set this country up for the AIDS epidemic by increasing the natural resistance to using condoms and other forms of safer sex. One gay man circumcised as an adult wrote:

---

* There are many safe-sex things to do with a partner, but if you're going to engage in anything that would result in exchange of semen or blood, it's better to use a good condom than to cut off a good foreskin. In the United States, there are no adequate federal standards for reliability. The free market reigns and the buyer should definitely beware—breakage rates vary tremendously, and "extra strength" on the label means nothing. The best source of information I know of is the March 1989 *Consumer Reports* article,"Can You Rely on Condoms?" *CR* would not grant permission to reprint the results in this book, so you'll have to rely on your local library and its photocopy machine or send $3 for reprint #RO85 to Reprints/Consumer Reports, P.O. Box 53016, Boulder, CO 80322.

Additional safer-sex information: nonoxynol-9 is a gentle detergent that in 1/2 to 1% concentrations effectively destroys viruses, including HIV, the virus believed to cause AIDS. It is now routinely added to many personal and condom lubricants and contraceptive gels and creams as a back-up safety factor. Many brands of moist "baby wipe" towelettes are impregnated with nonoxynol-9 (check labels in baby-care sections of supermarkets and pharmacies).

...about 75% of my sensitivity was gone...[T]he glans...almost ached for the protection of a warm sheath, which would never be possible again....Concerning anal sex, I was never 'big' on it....Now I seek it constantly; it is, in a way, a longing for the protecive sheath I have lost—along with its moisture and warmth."[11]

Some circumcised gay men also seek out intact lovers for "docking," placing penises end-to-end so that the foreskin of the intact penis can be shared with the bare glans of the circumcised one. It apparently never occurs to circumcisers that, by depriving men of full sexual sensation, they might actually be *encouraging* the very forms of sexual relating that are most risky —unprotected anal and vaginal intercourse. (Docking, although I haven't seen it rated in safer-sex information pamphlets, would seem to be a high risk activity, especially if done to orgasm.)

To get circumcised and still engage in unsafe sex with a potentially infected person would be to play a distinctly American version of Russian Roulette, and the illusion of safety could well make the epidemic worse. I can hear the conversations now in bedrooms, bars, and backseats across the country: "It's o.k., honey, we don't need the condom—I'm circumcised."

Ludicrous? Of course. But only slightly so, considering the extent to which we'll go to avoid coming to terms with the AIDS epidemic. Circumcision simply isn't any sort of "protective shield" against HIV, the virus believed to cause AIDS. Yet a few doctors—who in the last century might have prescribed it for asthma—are now encouraging circumcision as a preventive measure against AIDS. Faced with real or imagined foreskin conditions, we tend not to consider other, less drastic measures short of foreskin amputation. Specifically, teaching a boy about good hygiene and safer sex will serve him far better than cutting off a functional, highly sensitive part of his penis.

Physicians and medical associations abroad are generally strongly opposed to circumcision. In West Germany, doctors at the Frankfurt Army Medical Center are reportedly refusing to perform routine infant circumcisions.[12] Even in Canada, where the practice is still fairly common (though less so than in the United States), the Canadian Paediatric Society recently reviewed their existing policy against routine circumcision. After looking at the current research on the subject, they concluded:

> The present information available concerning the risks of urinary tract infections and transmission of sexually transmitted diseases in relation to circumcision is not sufficiently compelling to justify a change in policy.[13]

While national medical groups in the United States have expressed reservations about circumcision, none have come out in clear opposition (the Virginia Urologic Society is a notable exception on the state level—see page 31). Why? Romberg feels that, as with other medical practices, doctors' reluctance to stop circumcising has a lot more to do with the profit motive and their desire to be in control of their patients' health than with the various arguments around penile cancer, AIDS, or whatever.

> [M]any choices in human health care...have centered on who is in *control* and who is getting *paid*. A doctor is the person in *control* when he performs a circumcision. He cannot *control* whether or not that person is going to wash himself. Similarly, doctors get *paid* for doing circumcisions, but they do not get *paid* for telling people to wash.[14]

SO WHAT'S THE BIG DEAL, ANYWAY?

In a country where the great majority of men are circumcised, concern over the practice—and especially its implications for sexuality—is often viewed as making a mountain out of a molehill. "I'm doing fine with sex," a typical circumcised man will say, "so what's the big deal?"

The "big deal" has been understood for many centuries. Recognizing the sexual role of the foreskin, the great eleventh-century rabbi Moses Maimonides quite succinctly stated that the effect—indeed, a primary purpose—of circumcision was

> ...to limit sexual intercourse, and to weaken the organ of generation as far as possible, and thus cause man to be moderate.... for there is no doubt that circumcision weakens the power of sexual excitement, and sometimes lessens the natural enjoyment; the organ necessarily becomes weak when...deprived of its covering from the beginning. Our sages say distinctly: It is hard for a woman, with whom an uncircumcised [man] had sexual intercourse, to separate from him.
>
> —*Guide for the Perplexed*, Part III, Chapter XLIX

People with experience both ways tend to agree that a penis with a foreskin (its only moving part) is more fun to play with—and to *be* played with—than a circumcised one. This contributes toward pleasure in masturbation and sexual play with a partner. The foreskin keeps a man's natural lubrication from drying out (as happens with circumcised men), so that that the glans stays moist and sensitive, something that should be appreciated by anyone familiar with the pleasures of juicy kissing. Any circumcised man who knows the difference in feeling between masturbating "dry" versus with a personal lubricant can understand, by analogy, a *little* of what it might be like to have a soft, moist foreskin cuddling the glans and, during masturbation or sex play, stimulating it. And when the penis becomes erect it pushes out of this nerve-loaded sleeve of skin, so that what in the flaccid (soft) state is the sensitive inside of the foreskin becomes outside skin of the lengthened penis, covering up to a third or more of the entire penis shaft. It is this tissue, with its capacity for sensual communication and pleasure in contact with a partner's similar tissues, that circumcision slices away forever.

Just as the foreskin of ancient man protected his delicate glans from rough and thorny underbrush, in the modern world it protects it from the irritation of abrasive clothing and zippers. A permanently exposed glans of a circumcised penis dries up and develops, in the body's wisdom, a layer of nerveless skin called a *corneum*, which tries to perform the protective function of the foreskin. According to nationally syndicated radio and TV medical advisor Dr. Dean Edell, the corneum is 12 to 15 cell layers thick, compared with one or two layers for a glans constantly cuddled and protected by a moist foreskin. This is what separates the nerves in a man's glans from the moist, sensitive tissues of a sexual partner.

> The glans at birth is delicate and easily irritated by urine and feces. The foreskin shields the glans; with circumcision, this protection is lost. In such cases, the glans and especially the urinary opening (meatus) may become irritated or infected, causing ulcers, meatitis (inflammation of the meatus), and meatal stenosis (a narrowing of the urinary opening). Such problems virtually never occur in uncircumcised penises. The foreskin protects the glans throughout life.
>
> —American Academy of Pediatrics
> *Care of the Uncircumcised Penis* (brochure, 1984 version)

A constantly exposed glans, though considerably desensitized, is far more easily irritated by clothes and sheets than the foreskin that normally protects it would be. I've also noticed that when I cringe over seeing or hearing about a gory injury or a depiction of torture, it's my penis that does most of the cringing. More specifically, it's what is often euphemistically called the circumcision "scar"—more accurately, the foreskin stump— that responds in this way. The body remembers.

> For thousands of years, in many different cultures, the genitals have fallen victim to an amazing variety of mutilations and restrictions. For organs that are capable of giving us an immense amount of pleasure, they have been given an inordinate amount of pain.
>
> —Desmond Morris, *Body Watching*

How much sexual sensitivity remains after circumcision also depends on how much of the *frenulum* (also called *frenum*) was cut away or left. This is the fold of mucus membrane that attaches to the glans and the inside of the foreskin on the underside of the penis to keep the foreskin over the glans except when pulled back. It's loaded with nerves. As one man described it,

> I am not cut and all of my friends were, so I was very different....
> Even when I was very little...and I learned about circumcision, I wondered why something should be cut off that felt so good....
> [A]fter puberty...I could make myself come by just rubbing my frenum between my thumb and index finger, so the sensitivity is unquestionable.[15]

Varying degrees of the frenulum are cut away in circumcision. Many babies under the knife lose it all, some a chunk or two of their glans as well, and a few their sexual functionality, their penises, their health, even their lives.

While it may be impossible for us circumcised men to know what we're missing—and what the value of a foreskin would be—there *is* a way to get a definite hint. Here's how. With your penis in the flaccid state, lightly run a moistened finger, moving back a forth a little, from the tip of the glans (head of penis) up over the corona (rim of the glans), into the neck of the glans, across the circumcision "scar," and down the shaft. You'll probably notice that the circumcision "scar" is much more sensitive than the rest, even than the glans itself. That's some indication of what the whole inside of your foreskin—and, during erection, about a third of your shaft skin—might feel like if it hadn't been cut away. So when I hear other circumcised men say, "It feels so good now, I'm not sure if I could handle it if it was any better!" my personal reply is clear, immediate, and wistful: "I'd sure like to try!" Romberg raises an interesting point:

> Women complain that men are too "blunt" in their approach, "cut off" from their feelings....I suspect a connection [with circumcision].[16]

Considering how obsessed with sex (or at least sexual titillation) our society sometimes seems to be, why have our media (including feminist writers) not explored further this connection between circumcision and sexuality?

MEDIA MESSAGES

Mass media in *any* society tend to report more favorably and more fully whatever information supports the culture's values and practices. This can be seen in the way our newspapers and magazines report research findings and policy statements on circumcision. The American Academy of Pediatrics' 1989 revision of its long-standing position on circumcision is a case in point. For well over a decade, the AAP had maintained the fence-straddling position that "There is no absolute medical indication for routine circumcision of the newborn." On 6 March 1989 the organization released its long-awaited "new" position stating that "the procedure has *potential* medical benefits and advantages, as well as *inherent* disadvantages and risks" [emphases mine].

This is little changed from the previous position except in being wordier and more detailed. If anything, the new statement leans toward being anti-circumcision, since benefits are "potential," with risks being "inherent" (i.e., certain and unavoidable). AAP President Donald W. Schiff, M.D., has said, "We have not reversed our position. We've changed it a bit, but it's really just a bit."[17] Yet newspapers proclaimed this re-worded position with seriously one-sided reporting. Here are some examples of headlines clipped from papers around the country:[18]

"Pediatricians support circumcision: National group abandons previous stand on medical procedure"

"Circumcision policy eased: Doctors' group won't oppose routine practice"

"Pediatricians' statement gives limited approval to circumcision"

"Study backs circumcision to reduce disease"

"Group leans to circumcision: Pediatricians cite possible value"

"Pediatrics group sees benefit in circumcision of newborns"

"Doctors group reverses stance on medical benefits of circumcision"

"Circumcise: Pediatricians say it may not be so bad after all"

"Doctors give ground on circumcision"

"Circumcision: Clear Benefits, Some Risks"

"Academy changes position, calls circumcision beneficial"

"Circumcision Again Finds Favor With Doctors"

"Circumcision OK after all, pediatricians' group decides"

A story that ran in the *Ashbury Park Press* of Neptune, New Jersey, is an example of the sort of reporting used in schools of journalism to show what unprofessional propagandizing looks like. This newspaper received a fairly balanced Associated Press release on the AAP's new position and proceeded to edit out *all* references to disadvantages and risks, headlining the article, "Doctors find medical benefits in circumcision of newborns." Anyone reading the article would be left believing that there were clear benefits and *no* disadvantages or risks to infant circumcision. They didn't respond to a letter I wrote them about this.

Even publications that should (and perhaps do) know better went along with this wave of misrepresentation and deception of the public. *American Health*[19] ran an article in their Family Report section titled "Circumcision's comeback?" in which it was stated that the AAP had "reversed its earlier position" by saying "the procedure 'has potential medical benefits and advantages.'" In the whole of the full-page article, no mention whatsoever is made of the "inherent disadvantages and risks" clearly put forth in the AAP statement. It seems that we who are circumcised or who have circumcised our children—this includes newspaper editors and headline writers, as well as scientists, legislators, and judges who hear circumcision cases—*want* science to tell us that what has been done to us and what we have done to our children is good, or at least not damaging.

From the AAP report:[20]

Meatitis is more common in circumcised boys...

Evidence regarding the relationship of circumcision to sexually transmitted diseases is conflicting.

[O]ne study shows...a higher incidence of nonspecific urethritis in circumcised men.

The exact incidence of post-operative complications is not known.

Local anesthesia adds an element of risk.

And, in a sad example of how doctors often use scientific terminology to distance themselves from the reality of medical procedures, the report understates trauma by noting that

Infants undergoing circumcision without anesthesia demonstrate physiologic responses suggesting they are experiencing pain.

FEMALE CIRCUMCISION

Most people in Western society are unaware that females can be circumcised. Many think the idea is a joke. When made aware of the reality of the practice, most find it repugnant. Yet the origins of female circumcision and the justifications for its practice are very much similar to those of male circumcision.

—Rosemary Romberg, *Circumcision: The Painful Dilemma*

The U.S. public and medical professions may well be shaken out of their complacency and gain a new perspective on male circumcision when the United States is hit by the same storm of controversy that has already raged through parts of Europe, where increasing immigration from Central African, Islamic, and Arabic countries has brought the practice of female circumcision into the arena of political debate. A harrowing account of her own pre-puberty circumcision by Nawal el Saadawi, M.D, from her book *The Hidden Face of Eve: Women in the Arab World*, can be found in Appendix C of this book. Dr. Saadawi was fired as director of education in the Egyptian Ministry of Health and editor of *Health* magazine for publishing her book *Women and Sex* in a society which is not accustomed to open discussion of sexuality, especially women's. Female circumcision in cultures in which it is practiced is a much more severe form of genital mutilation than male circumcision as practiced in the United States. (Information on female circumcision worldwide can be obtained from Women's International Network, Appendix A.)

A narrow definition of female circumcision would be surgical removal of the clitoral hood, but the term is commonly used in a broader sense to include all female genital mutilations, such as *clitoridectomy* (removal of part or all of the clitoris, as in Dr. Saadawi's case) or, as in the Sudan, *vulvectomy* (removal of the inner and/or outer vaginal lips) and *infibulation*, sewing up of the vagina, leaving only a small opening for the passage of menstrual blood. An infibulated woman may have to be cut open for marriage (or ripped open by her husband's penis) and for childbirth, and re-sewn if her husband dies or after childbirth. A whole class of women subsists from the performance of these procedures (in Egypt, many untrained men make their living performing clitoridectomies in unhygienic street stalls). Some women working against clitoridectomy in their own countries have reacted negatively to the use of the emotionally loaded term "genital mutilation" by horrified Westerners, maintaining that "circumcision" is a more acceptable word. And many women assert their *right* to continue this practice on their daughters in societies where mutilation with its implications for sexual docility and controlability is a prerequisite for marriage and therefore economic survival.

While female circumcision is not common in western societies, neither has it been unknown. Removal of the clitoral hood has been prescribed by some doctors as a way to bring unruly sexual appetites under control and by others for the opposite effect, as a way to increase sexual sensation by keeping the clitoris constantly exposed. Desmond Morris, in his book *Body Watching*, in the chapter on "The Genitals," cites a Texas doctor who, as late as 1937, was advocating removal of the clitoris as a cure for frigidity. The Winter 1989-90 issue of the NOCIRC Newsletter, in an item headed "Female Circumcision in America," cites other cases of female circumcision in the United States:

> In 1955, the clitoris and labia were removed from a 12-year old Baltimore girl who now, at 47, has just learned that the statute of

limitations prevents her from taking legal action against the doctor who caused her physical and psychological damage.

A gynecologist who performed experimental genital surgery on 33 women without their knowledge lost his license to practice last year after a CBS News report exposed his 'love surgery.' The experimental operations, including circumcision, resulted in complaints by the women of sexual dysfunction similar to complaints made my many circumcised men.

While most forms of female circumcision are more drastic than what men in the United States experience, male circumcision also varies in severity, in some societies involving partial castration (removal of one testicle) or *subincision*— slitting the entire underside of the penis to the urethra and splaying it out. Perhaps the most severe form of male circumcision has been

> stripping of the skin from the navel to the anus, including the skin of the penis and scrotum of a young bridegroom.[21]

> The one being circumcised may not cry out nor wail or he would be despised and forsaken by his bride, who witnesses the procedure. Hot oil is put on the wound. People often die of the consequences, many leave the tribe.[22]

Every society which circumcises females also does it to the males, though the reverse is not true—most societies which practice male circumcision do not circumcise the females. Male circumcision, in other words, is more common, and it apparently preceded female circumcision historically. In almost all cultures which circumcise males and/or females, it is performed on teens or pre-teens, as in Islam today.

Wherever it's practiced, female circumcision tends to be more common among the poorer people, yet even a good number of more affluent, educated people continue the practice. In her book *Gyn Ecology: The Metaphysics of Radical Feminism*, Mary Daly writes of an interview a Danish scholar had with a young Egyptian woman physician who was expecting a baby.

> She informed him that "if the child she was expecting should be a girl she would circumcise her herself." The young woman gave several reasons. The first was religious: she was a muslim [*sic*]. The second was cosmetic: she wanted "to remove something

disfiguring, ugly and repulsive." Thirdly, the girl should be protected from sexual stimulation through the clitoris. The fourth reason was tradition.[23]

Unlike most Westerners who have their sons circumcised, this woman was prepared to personally perform the operation on her daughter. Perhaps out of her fear of her own surgically muted sexual energy, she clearly intended to partially destroy her daughter's sexual response "for her own good." For this degree of forthrightness about *male* circumcision we have to turn to Maimonides (see quote, page 22), because most people today who circumcise baby *boys* do not do it with the intent (at least not the *conscious* intent) to decrease their sexuality. Otherwise, though, the reasons this physician gives for her intent to circumcise her daughter are hauntingly similar to those frequently given for circumcising baby boys.

Female circumcision abroad has long been a feminist concern in the West, while male genital mutilation goes on in our own backyard all the time. In the immigrant controversy in Europe, Britain has banned female circumcision with an Act of Parliament, while France has applied already-existing child abuse laws to accomplish the same goal. In Italy, the national health service has stirred up a storm of controversy by deciding to actually perform clitoridectomies on request, on the grounds that if they don't, parents will have the procedure done at home, with the attendant risks of serious infections and of girls bleeding to death (such a case in France led to the application of child abuse laws).[24] Though most of those who practice female circumcision drop it when they immigrate to the United States (although they continue male circumcision), it's only a matter of time until some enterprising journalist probes into an immigrant community or kinship group where it's practiced, opening up a potentially far-reaching debate. The outraged comments that will ensue will almost surely include anti-Arab sentiments. This explosion of public feeling will provide a unique opportunity for the preservationist movement—through letters to the editor, calls to talk shows, discussions with family and friends, public demonstrations—to defuse the racism and help open people's eyes and hearts to the tragedy of *all* genital mutilation, male as well as female, at home as well as abroad.

OLD SOLDIERS

Dr. Aaron J. Fink, a retired urologist from California, has emerged as the most colorful and outspoken of the modern-day circumcisionists. He and his followers denounce preservationists as "foreskin fundamentalists" or "foreskin fanatics." He's sometimes invited to participate in television and radio debates, and has written a small book on circumcision. I've met Dr. Fink briefly; he seems to be a sincere and dedicated man. He became concerned, he told me, when he heard a preservationist doctor give some inaccurate information on television. He wrote to him, but the reply came instead from the head of the national preservationist organization NOCIRC (see Appendix A). Dr. Fink, alarmed that there was an actual movement out there—"a network," he calls it in a lowered voice, as if it were a dangerous conspiracy—decided to speak out and to write and self-publish his book, *Circumcision: A Parent's Decision for Life*, which is a compilation of historical arguments in support of infant circumcision.

On the other side of the issue, the Virginia Urologic Society in 1986 viewed documentation of a circumcision case which led to "loss of all the skin of the penile shaft" and another resulting in "gangrene and necrosis of the entire glans and penis due to electrocautery." James L. Snyder, M.D., past President of the Society, was called in for consultation on these two injuries. "I can tell you," he says, "that both of these children will be lifetime genital cripples."[25] As a result of these two cases, the Virginia Urologic Society unanimously passed a resolution against routine infant circumcision and is planning to bring the issue before the Virginia Medical Association and ultimately the American Medical Association, which has never taken a stand one way or the other on this most common of all surgeries.

Cruel and innane medical practices, like old soldiers, seem not to die, but to fade slowly away. As more and more babies are left intact to become men who appreciate the value of a foreskin, this debate, too, will pass the way of those over blood-letting and routine tonsillectomy.

It bears repeating that even now, as it has been throughout history, circumcision is a cultural, not a medical, phenomenon. Circumcisionist Dr. Fink in his book gives four *non*-medical arguments in favor of circumcision: training, economics, culture, and convenience.[26] Underlying all his arguments is the belief that circumcision doesn't involve any significant loss, though to his credit he does acknowledge it hurts. Here, in brief, are his arguments:

Training: In order for the nation to have an ample supply of doctors adequately trained in circumcision, Dr. Fink maintains, we need to keep the circumcision rate up—for practice, so to speak.

Economics. Surgery on an adult is more complex because of more bleeding, the necessity of stitches, and a separate hospital appointment. It also requires counseling and usually general anesthesia—in short, permission of and consideration for the patient. For these reasons, it's cheaper to cut off the foreskins of all male babies than those of the 5 to 10% of boys and men in the United States who will wind up getting therapeutic circumcisions for one reason or another.

Culture. The mere fact that circumcision is widespread—that a child's father or playmates are circumcised—is, in and of itself, sufficient reason to circumcise a child. "Parents may wish their son to be like his father or like other boys,"[27] writes Dr. Fink.

Convenience. The title of one short subsection of Dr. Fink's book sums up this argument: "Circumcision makes it easy to keep the penis clean."[28]

A CLOSER LOOK

The following is a brief critique of these non-medical arguments:

Training. If we're going to do mass circumcisions just to keep doctors in practice, then we might as well have plenty of plane crashes in order to keep our rescue teams in shape, or encourage consumption of meat, milk, and eggs so that our heart surgeons can keep their skills well-honed. Clearly, if we didn't routinely circumcise, we wouldn't *need* so many doctors trained to do it.

Economics. U.S. figures for therapeutically necessary adult circumcisions are much higher than, say, in Europe. Doctors here tend to think immediately of amputating the foreskin whenever they see even a minor problem with it because they quite literally don't know what else to do, while their European counterparts would be much more likely to first try non-intrusive or less-drastic treatments (previously mentioned) that can usually solve the problem.

At any rate, placing a monetary value on our healthy body parts is an outrage. If we could cut the cost of treating breast cancer in adult women by removing the breast tissue of all baby girls, would that justify routine preventive infant mastectomy? Of course not. I, for one, would not want my foreskin, if I still had one, to be amputated as a cost-cutting measure for Blue Shield or Medicare. (In fact, Medicare in several states and a number of insurance companies have stopped covering routine infant circumcisions, while continuing to pay for therapeutically necessary ones. The latest group to save valuable health-care dollars by cutting costs instead of penises is the State of Washington, which no longer pays for unnecessary circumcision of its employees' children.[29])

In summary, "therapeutic" circumcision, while occasionally really necessary, is in most cases a gross overreaction.

Culture. The American Academy of Pediatrics has observed that "In addition to the medical aspects, other factors will affect the parent's decisions, including aesthetics, religion, cultural attitudes, social pressures, and tradition."[30] It's disappointing that the drafters of this statement didn't have the insight or political courage to declare that these are *not* valid reasons for surgically removing a healthy, highly sensitive, functional part of a child's body. By their implicit acceptance of these reasons, they are complicit in routine violation of their own medical code of ethics, based in the Hippocratic Oath: "First, to do no harm..." Still, they are neutral. Dr. Fink goes beyond this morally questionable neutrality, saying it's *o.k.* to circumcise a baby boy for cosmetic reasons. This gets to the core of the issue, since the single most common reason parents give for having their sons circumcised is not health, nor religion, but simply because they "wish their son to be like his father or like other boys."

The same logic, of course, would have applied as well to foot-binding of young girls in pre-revolutionary China and would apply to partial male castration or female genital mutilation as practiced in a number of cultures today. Would Dr. Fink condone such practices rather than have boys and girls go through the real or imagined trauma of being "different"? Apparently so, if he were or had been a member of those societies. This brings up two fundamental questions: When cultural habits are found to be in conflict with biological integrity, which should prevail? And who has the right to make that decision, the parent or the child slated to have his body mutilated?

If we look beneath the surface of expressed concern about a child "fitting in," we can often unmask more troubling motivations. The very thought of leaving their sons intact can often be threatening to circumcised men and their mates.

> What was so difficult in leaving my son intact was not that my son would feel different in a locker room, but that I would feel different from him. I would then have to accept that I'm an amputee from the wars of a past generation.[31]

Every child, every person, is going to be different from others in many ways. We wouldn't cut off a boy's finger just because his father lost one in a war or an industrial accident, so surely we can refrain from depriving him of his foreskin just because his father has been so deprived. Yet most of us have never thought to question circumcision, perhaps because it's easier to continue the practice than to face our own loss. With reflection, we can see that we don't have to do this. Instead, we can tell our circumcised and intact sons that people used to think it was necessary or good to circumcise, but now we know better—a simple, truthful, no-nonsense, no-trauma explanation.

Convenience. There is a sad logic, though a thin one, to the argument that a circumcised penis is easier to keep clean, especially since most fathers and doctors themselves were deprived of their foreskins, have no experience in the very simple practice of cleaning an intact penis, and perhaps don't want to be reminded of what they've lost by helping boys learn to clean their natural penses. But wouldn't it make more sense for doctors and parents to learn how to educate intact boys rather than to cut off part of the babies' genitals? If someone were to suggest that we cut off children's noses, excise their ears, or pull their teeth just to make the job of cleaning their bodies easier, we would think they were joking. If they were actually going to *do* such things to a child, we would call on the authorities to intervene and have them put in psychiatric counseling. Yet Dr. Fink, a member of prestigious medical associations, can with impunity put forth "convenience" as a valid reason for cutting off someone else's foreskin—just to make it easier to keep the penis clean.

Even circumcision "hawks," however, draw back from the logical implications of their own arguments—routine circumcision of all males, including adults. As Dr. Fink states in his book:

> I'm not urging or even encouraging that uncircumcised adult men rush out and have a preventive circumcision. An adult is well aware of his personal hygiene, his sexual habits, and the risk, if any, of his acquiring a sexually transmitted disease. But for a newborn, the case is different. In deciding whether to have a son circumcised, parents are making a choice that may be of great consequence throughout his entire life.[32]

If we were to grab off the street and forcefully circumcise the most slovenly man, someone who engages in unsafe sex and never practices penile hygiene, people would be horrified. It would be condemned as an assault and a violation of his basic human rights. Yet we accept as normal doing the same thing to helpless babies whose future habits we don't know but can greatly influence through teaching and personal example. The difference, of course, is that an adult has the legal right and power to say no, and the capacity to physically resist. A baby has neither legal right nor sufficient physical strength to ward off the assault.

RIGHTS

So circumcision boils down to a matter of personal and cultural choice, but—and this is crucial—*it should be the personal and cultural choice of the one being circumcised*, not of the parents. We men have as much right to our bodies as women do to theirs, a right which in the United States is routinely violated.

The Articles of Convention of the International Save the Children Fund places the organization "against all forms of

physical and mental injury to children",[33] while both the pain of
and the loss resulting from circumcision are in violation of
Article 5 of the Universal Declaration of Human Rights, adopted
by the United Nations General Assembly on 10 December 1948,
and binding on all member states, including the United States:

> No one shall be subjected to torture or to cruel, inhuman or
> degrading treatment...

If not for our cultural bias, we could see that cutting off part of a
baby's genitals, especially without anesthesia, is "cruel treatment," as is compromising an adult's sexuality. But it's not
likely that either the Save the Children Fund or the United
Nations will come out against circumcision since the practice is
common in the United States, which provides much of their
support (though the UN, despite accusations of "cultural
imperialism," has reportedly begun to address the more extreme
forms of female circumcision.)

U.S. courts have not so far been very protective of baby
boys' genitals. Several cases have been brought, including one
by a rabbi's wife against the *mohel* (Jewish ritual circumciser)
who circumcised her son against her will and another on behalf
of a baby boy who was circumcised without his mother being
adequately informed about the operation before signing the
consent form. Legal issues can involve battery, false imprison-
ment, sexual assault, and (since circumcision is a "nonaccidental
physical injury") child abuse; informed consent (whether the
parent has been adequately informed about the procedure before
giving their consent); and infant rights (whether the parent even
has the right to consent to surgery on a baby who has no medical
problem that requires it).

In Britain, a four-year-old Muslim boy has been awarded
£10,000 (about $17,000) provisional damages from the rabbi
who botched his circumcision, necessitating three corrective
surgeries. The court said the award will be later increased if the
boy develops psychological or sexual problems after puberty.[34]

Preservationist organizations have not had enough funds for
well-researched cases and multiple appeals, and so no precedent
has been set that would protect baby boys. It's not surprising
that the courts have been reluctant to rule in favor of male
infants' fundamental right to intact genitals, for to do so would

be to make criminals out of prestigious members of the powerful medical profession. It would also raise politically explosive issues of religious freedom and separation of church and state. And the courts are no more willing to apply international law (such as the Universal Declaration of Human Rights cited above) to the practice of genital mutilation than they are to hear challenges to nuclear deterrence, which, as a threat of "mass and indiscriminate destruction" of civilian populations, is also illegal under international law. The result of this timidity of the courts is that parents can have their children surgically mutilated without the courts intervening *as long as the mutilation is a traditional and commonly accepted one.* (Contact NOCIRC, Appendix A, for specific and current legal information.)

Courts and law enforcement personnel are seldom willing to go out on a limb by bucking entrenched social prejudices, but we can find encouragement from looking at the history of other modern social reform movements. As the social and political climate around this issue continues to change—through education and outreach as well as more dramatic acts of public protest and civil disobedience—we can expect that legal decisions will start to shift. What is now controversial—the idea that babies' genitals should be left in their natural state—will then seem obvious.

> All truth passes through three stages. First, it is ridiculed. Second, it is violently opposed. Third, it is accepted as being self-evident.
> —Schopenhauer

It's quite sobering—especially for men—to realize that if what is routinely done to baby boys started being done to baby girls in the United States (see Appendices C and D), there would be a great hue and cry and very legitimate charges of child abuse. But we've come to accept *male* genital mutilation as normal. The force of tradition has shut out our cries at our own violation, our mutilation, and we've adapted to the silent denial. At my first venture into the men's movement—at the 13th Annual Conference on Men and Masculinity (Seattle, 1988)—men in the "activist caucus" were planning a demonstration at a nearby porno theater to protest the violence depicted against women. The group seemed largely unreceptive to concerning themselves with circumcision and a conference workshop on the subject was attended by only a handful of the hundreds present.

NITTY GRITTY

There in Seattle on that day—on any day, in any city or town—a great number of 24- to 48-hour-old baby boys (some older) were velcro-strapped down on molded plastic boards actually brand-named "Circumstraints" designed specifically to hold them immobile while their most sensitive tissues are efficiently and traumatically sliced off. This usually happens in the nursery, or a room nearby. It happens to over a million baby boys in the United States every year, some 3,300 every day.[35]

As mentioned previously, infant circumcision is performed without anesthetic—general anesthetic is too dangerous to use routinely for minor surgery on babies; spray anesthetics are very ineffective; and injections into the penis (rarely done) are only partly effective and are themselves highly traumatic. After the baby is strapped down, an antiseptic is applied to the genital area, and a paper or cloth drape is placed over the baby's body with a hole exposing the genitals, much like a rubber dental dam is used by a dentist to obscure all parts of the mouth except the tooth being worked on. Before it can be cut off, the baby's foreskin has to be separated from the glans. (Nature, left to herself, separates them gently over a number of years.) A probe is forced under the foreskin and moved around the glans, tearing them apart. This is when the baby usually starts to scream. The loosened foreskin is then slit with surgical scissors. The screams intensify, and the baby's heart rate increases dramatically; he may go into a comatose state to escape the pain, a state often mistaken for sleep. Some babies vomit or defecate. What happens next depends on the type of device used. In one procedure, a little cone or "bell" device is then placed over the raw glans to protect it. The foreskin is stretched over the outside of the cone and tied, then cut off, circular fashion, around the cone, with a scalpel. Alternatively, the Gomco clamp is used to crush the foreskin against the cone for 3–5 minutes, lessening bleeding while the foreskin is amputated. The wound is dressed and the baby begins a healing period of up to a week. His penis is swollen and tender, urine burns the wound, and abrasion of diapers causes additional pain and discomfort. If the Plastibell device is used, it is left on for a week to ten days until the foreskin, deprived of a blood supply, falls off, leaving no wound to dress. (See Appendix D for a nurse's eye-witness account of a circumcision.)

SEXUAL ASSAULT

What's clearly a men's issue also has implications not only for women with babies to protect but for heterosexual women in terms of physical sensation during lovemaking. (Sadly, quite a few American women, though sexually experienced, have never even seen an intact penis, while a few, unaccustomed to them, find them repugnant.) Most Americans, men and women, are as unaware of the negative consequences of male circumcision as people in many Arabic and African countries are that female circumcision is an abomination. The increasing public understanding about the implications of widespread child sexual abuse in the United States—something like one in four girls, one in six boys—contrasts with our bland acceptance of the fact that a full 58% of U.S. infant males, over a fourth of all children, experience extreme genital violence in the form of circumcision during the totally vulnerable preverbal period of infancy. Custom and ritual help those who perpetrate the violence avoid the full impact of what they're doing, but do they help the victims? Or is the social acceptance of this mutilation, sometimes even a pride in it, a profound disempowerment of the violated, a denial of very real and intense pain at the time and later sexual loss?

Just as members of any historically violated or oppressed group (women, slaves, children, industrial workers) adapt to and often wind up identifying with the very system responsible for their pain and their limitations, so do we as men do to our sons what was done to us—as noted earlier, the most common reason given by parents for circumcising their baby boys is so the child will look like Dad (or other boys). (Not all men, though, adapt in this way. See Appendix E for comments from men who resent their circumcised state.) Lack of awareness and actual denial are widespread—most men don't realize what they've lost or are understandably reluctant to admit it even to themselves, much less to publicly proclaim it and risk scorn or ridicule. As for parents, who wants to admit what they've allowed to be done to their sons? And just as male rapists are often surprised to learn that their victims actually suffered, that they really did mean "no," doctors are numbed to the babies' only way of attempting to withhold their consent—with their struggles and their screams. Until recently, in fact, when it became "scientifically proved" that babies feel pain, many doctors steadfastly maintained that they didn't, and major surgeries were performed without anesthesia.

Rape, of course, is not motivated by the same feelings as is our culture's routine surgical assault on the genitals of infant males. To say that would be over-simplistic. Still, there *are* parallels: both are acts against a victim's will, both involve the genitals, both cause physical pain and emotional trauma, both are supported by myths which help those who do it deny the reality of what they're doing, and both can be seen as ways to teach the victim, through pain and fear, her or his proper role in the patriarchal (male-dominated) order of things. As one circumcised man put it (from Appendix E),

> Fear, pain, crippling, disfigurement and humiliation are classic ways to break the human spirit. Circumcision includes them all.

The unstudied implications of circumcision are broad, with many unanswered questions: What about our resistance as men to admitting our sensitivities, part of which we've physically lost? How much guilt do we have around the penis, rather than feeling wholesome and good about it? Penises (both circumcised and intact) are not infrequently referred to and even used as weapons, as instruments of domination and control. How does circumcision affect our potential to love and respect our penises, our bodies, and our partners? And how do other aspects of our lives affect our response to circumcision? In one study of cultures that practice male circumcision, it was found that it was done more frequently (64% vs. 20–22%) among those families in which the father slept separately from the mother and child.[36] This would seem to indicate that the integration of men with women and children tends to inhibit genital mutilations even when socially accepted or approved.

While scientific studies on the sexual, psychological, and social effects of circumcision are almost nonexistent, that's beginning to change. Men circumcised after their eighteenth birthday are now being sought to participate in a study on the effects of circumcision. Interested readers can contact:

George Dennison, M.D.
2442 N.W. Market Street
Seattle, WA 98107

There are also people who work specifically helping men to get in touch with their repressed circumcision traumas, to discharge their pent-up pain and rage, to let go of the sense of powerlessness they were given so long ago, and finally to heal the deep and lingering wounds left by their genital mutilation. One couple in Utah, Frederick and Jeannine Parvati Baker,[37] conduct workshops around the country to heal sexual trauma, in which ritual and myth are often used to relive the birth and post-birth experience, this time with a gentle welcoming into the world.

"The direct verbal approach can only access later trauma," they say. "Circumcision happens before a child is verbal and requires a non-verbal approach."

The Pre- and Peri-natal Psychology Association of North America (PPPANA) is concerned with the issue, and a number of counselors in Re-evaluation Counseling ("co-counseling") are working within their respective communities to end routine "medical" and ritual circumcision.

In England, Ya'acov Khan[38] conducts workshops using dance, voice, drumming, and ritual to access and heal various wounds, including circumcision.

WHY NOT?—A SUMMARY

So what's wrong with routine infant circumcision? Why shouldn't parents have their baby boys circumcised? I can think of at least ten reasons:

1. It hurts—trauma inflicted on a primary pleasure center.

2. It can result in serious complications.

3. It can leave psychological scars.

4. It's done against the will of the person it's done to.

5. It dries up a man's natural lubrication.

6. It makes the glans less sensitive and sex less pleasurable.

7. By removing its only moving part, it makes the penis less fun to play with and to be played with.

8. It can cause a son to resent his parents for depriving him of his full and natural sexuality (see Appendix E).

9. Because it decreases sensation and because people seek pleasure in sex, it can encourage unprotected intercourse —poor public health policy in the age of AIDS.

10. For over a hundred years, it's been a surgery in search of a justification. Knowing its history generates skepticism (at best) about the latest medical "reasons" for doing it.

On the other hand, you may still feel there are valid reasons *to* circumcise. I invite you to list them here:

1.

2.

3.

4.

5.

6.

7.

8.

9.

10.

When you're finished, compare the two lists, weigh the considerations both ways, and decide for yourself, bearing in mind that the same freedom to decide that you enjoy might be valued by infant boys whose genitals are at stake.

Religion and Spirituality

THE RELIGIOUS RITE

Cautiously, almost apologetically, I broached the subject of circumcision with a pregnant Jewish friend, painfully aware that because of anti-Semitism in our society—her own family had been harassed by the Ku Klux Klan—criticism of circumcision is often viewed as (and sometimes is) anti-Semitic. I was relieved when she thanked me for my concern. As a child, she'd been present at the *bris millah* (naming ceremony and ritual circumcision) of a cousin, and had been deeply shocked and very glad she wasn't a boy. "I'd *never* do that to *my* child," she said. "I don't care *who* says I should." An experience in her childbirth classes reinforced her instinctive response:

> One of the parents gave birth early and we saw the baby. He'd been circumcised and I watched as she changed his diaper. The end of his penis was so raw, and the urine stung the end of the penis every time he peed. Well, when you're a newborn, you pee all the time! So this poor little kid, what're his first experiences of his penis? For the first part of his life it's all pain. I mean, it must affect him psychologically, and I think his sexuality. I don't see how it couldn't.[39]

My friend's baby turned out to be a boy, and I was invited to a gentle Hebrew and English welcoming and naming ceremony and party with lots of friends and food, a sort of alternative bris without the surgery. "I'll raise him as a cultural Jew," my friend says proudly of her new son, "and when he's older the choice will be his."

A small but growing number of American Jews are choosing the option of a *bris shalom,* a naming ceremony of peace rather than surgery. (One innovative couple whacked off the tip of an

organic carrot instead of their son's foreskin.) The Alternative
Bris Support Group (see Appendix A) is working to transform
the ritual into a humane one, and some boys have gone through
their bar mitzvahs intact. Circumcision is an open question for
the Society of Humanistic Judaism, whose Summer 1988 issue
of *Humanistic Judaism* (Appendix A) dealt extensively with the
practice in terms of health, civil liberties (infant and body
rights), and feminism—that is, as a naming ceremony
exclusively for boys, it is inherently patriarchal and sexist. This
latter criticism can be overcome in three ways: by circumcising
both boys and girls; by eliminating the ceremony altogether; or
by having a nonsurgical naming ceremony for both.

(This feminist criticism focuses on the social validation the
bris gives. A medical, sexual, or men's rights criticism would
focus on the biologically negative aspect: that to cut of part of
boys' genitals but not girls' is sexist against males. All these
concerns, as well as those about cultural integrity and
continuity, would be satisfied by a nonsurgical bris for both
girls and boys.)

The original form of Jewish infant circumcision apparently
removed only the tip of the foreskin, with today's typically
"tight" (i.e., more severe or radical) circumcision being the
rabbinate's response to large numbers of Jewish men practicing
foreskin restoration through stretching what was left in a variety
of ingenious ways. Although attempts at getting it back are
probably as old as the practice of cutting it off, for a long time
restoration wasn't done in large enough numbers to be a cultural
threat (or a threat to patriarchal religious authority). This
changed under the Greeks, when Jewish men felt ashamed to
appear in the nude games and public baths with partially
exposed glans, and later, during the fifth century CE (Common
Era), to avoid Roman taxes on identifiable Jews. [Romberg
refers to the Jewish switch to "tight" circumcision as beginning
under the Greeks, whereas Mark Waring in *Foreskin
Restoration (Uncircumcision)* identifies it as starting under the
Romans.] These were the first and second historic periods of
foreskin restoration. The third period was during Hitler's reign
of terror, when a man's ritual circumcision scar was a death
warrant for the entire family. Restorative surgery was often

attempted and frequently botched. The fourth, which we are now entering, involves both Jews and (primarily American) gentiles and is rooted in increased knowledge about the harmful and limiting effects of circumcision; both stretching and surgical techniques are being used. (This is dealt with later in this book as well as in Appendix B.)

WHOLLY WRIT

This is my covenant, which ye shall keep, between me and you and thy seed after thee; Every man child among you shall be circumcised.

And ye shall circumcise the flesh of your foreskin; and it shall be a token of the covenant betwixt me and you.

And he that is eight days old shall be circumcised among you, every man child in your generations, he that is born in thy house, or bought with money of any stranger, which is not of thy seed.

He that is born in thy house, and he that is bought with thy money, must needs be circumcised: and my covenant shall be in your flesh for an everlasting covenant.

And the uncircumcised man child whose flesh of his foreskin is not circumcised, that soul shall be cut off from his people; he hath broken my covenant.

—Genesis 17:11–14

Both Judaism and Islam have a tradition of circumcision of infants and adolescents, respectively. In many Islamic countries, both boys and girls are circumcised, the girls more severely. Female circumcision, absorbed from African societies into which Islam spread, was never given a scriptural basis but is often considered to have religious significance. Christianity, which started out as a Jewish sect, went through internal struggle between pro- and anti-circumcision factions over whether to require circumcision for membership. The intact forces won out, perhaps because circumcision would have been a major disincentive for conversion to this new proselytizing religion. Only baptism was required, though there are many Christians today who believe circumcision is required or at least looked upon favorably by God. "Jesus was circumcised, wasn't he?" people ask in emulation, forgetting that he was also nailed to a cross, something most parents aren't eager to have done to their children.

Baptism itself may have derived from ancient rites in which priests smeared themselves with the blood of a circumcision or an animal sacrifice, or mixed the blood with water and washed themselves.[40] (Contact Peaceful Beginnings, Appendix A, for information on circumcision and Christianity.)

Many Jews are equally unaware of what circumcision is and isn't, what it does and doesn't do. On hearing that a Jewish mother's baby boy isn't circumcised, they might remark, "Then he isn't Jewish." While circumcising an infant son might arguably make a parent (not the child) a more *observant* Jew, Jewishness itself comes (except for converts) simply from having a Jewish mother, no more, no less. (Many in Reform Judaism trace Jewishness through the father as well.) While being circumcised is often perceived as an essential part of Jewish cultural identity, there are Jewish men—including those born in Europe during the Holocaust who were left intact as a way to help them survive—who are considered Jews nonetheless. And the uncircumcised state of Jewish women doesn't keep them from being or feeling Jewish.

> It is not a sacrament, and any child born of a Jewish mother is a Jew, whether circumcised or not.
> —*Encyclopaedia Judaica* (CIRCUMCISION: Laws)[41]

Nonetheless, for Jews the bris is a covenant (contract or agreement). For the religiously orthodox (fundamentalist), it's a restatement of the Covenant between God and Abraham, and all of Abraham's descendants (and their slaves—"bought with money of any stranger"). As such, the requirement for circumcision is as unquestionable as the existence of the devil is for a Christian fundamentalist. For the more humanistic or secular, the covenant is one of culture, of bonding with diverse others who share in common a many-faceted ancient tradition. This social and psychological function of the bris is usually strong enough to override parental concerns about pain, future sexuality, and risks of serious complications. Edward Wallerstein, author of the book *Circumcision: An American Health Fallacy*, has summed up this cultural attachment:

> Having conducted dozens of discussions on this subject, I have found one reaction typical among Jewish physicians. I will paraphrase their comments: "I agree that there are no health benefits.

I even feel that it may be wrong to do it. Yet, if I have a son, I will have him circumcised. Please don't ask me why. I am not in the least bit religious. I know it is irrational, but I will do it."[42]

There is also scriptural basis for animal sacrifice and authorizing parents to have a son stoned to death if he turns out bad. And the same part of the Bible that mandated Jewish circumcision also required Abraham to circumcise all his slaves, implying that God approved of slavery. As historical conditions change, so do our attitudes toward formerly accepted practices.

While there's no simple explanation for the complex cultural phenomenon of ritual circumcision—for most, both Jews and non-Jews, it's "just done"—several considerations may shed light on why it has survived so long within Judaism, not only among fundamentalists but among Jews generally. They fall into the categories of patriarchy, dogma, and cultural resistance.

ROOTS AND FRUITS OF VIOLENCE

Patriarchy. Despite current feminist challenges and some indications of a distant past in which women were more honored and powerful—for example, Jewishness coming through the mother—Judaism is essentially patriarchal. (Circumcision is apparently practiced only in patriarchal societies in which there are groups with a vested interest in the practice—for orthodox Jews, the mohelim, or ritual circumcisers; for all of us, the modern priesthood of physicians.)

As in numerous other societies, Jewish circumcision probably originated as part of a pre-Hebraic puberty rite, a blood ritual, perhaps because men were envious of girls' awesome natural initiation into adulthood through menstruation and child-bearing. (Even today, in the rare cases in which a boy is born without a foreskin, blood must still be drawn in the ceremony.) In some cultures, this imitation of females is clear. Many Australian aborigines who have subincised penises (see page 29) strap them up to their bellies so they will resemble vaginas; some reopen the subincision wound from time to time so they can "menstruate."[43] In his book *Symbolic Wounds: Puberty Rites and the Envious Male,* Bruno Bettelheim argues that with the development of pre-Hebraic culture into a paternalistic monotheism (religion with a single father-figure god), circumcision changed into a procedure performed on infants, reflecting the absolute submission of humans to the new, all-powerful male god.[44] (The modern-day bar mitzvah may be a remnant of an ancient adolescent circumcision ceremony.) Just as loving, otherwise nurturing parents turn their male child over to a man to have trauma inflicted on a primary pleasure center, so this new male god was both loving and vengeful.

If female circumcision existed in this pre-Hebraic culture, it was dropped as the new religion developed. Romberg raises the question of whether, under the developing patriarchal system, mothers had enough social clout to protect their baby daughters but not enough to protect their "more important" infant sons.

Infant circumcision also has to do with social control. If a parent can be made—through force, religious injunction, social pressure, fear of ostracism, or inculcation of a belief that it is beneficial to the child—to hand over a precious newborn baby to have his or her genitals mutilated by a medical or religious priesthood, then those parents are firmly under the control of that group. In addition, a rebellious adolescent can potentially put up a lot of resistance to having his (or her) genitals cut on, whereas a baby is helpless—a baby can only scream, but a teenager can scream *and* fight *and* run. So doing it to infants is less disruptive than doing it to older children, especially children who have been exposed to the ways of other cultures which leave the genitals intact. Many might well rebel or defect rather than be circumcised.

The relationship of circumcision with patriarchy and war may be speculative, but the September 1989 issue of *National Geographic*, in an article retracing the Christian crusades through the Arabic lands, contained an interesting juxtaposition of two photographs (which I tried unsuccessfully to obtain permission to reprint here). One shows men on horses throwing spear-like objects at each other. From the caption: "Playing at war, elders of central Turkey preserve the game *cirit*, a galloping exchange of blunt lances enjoyed...around the time of the Crusades." The other shows a boy, looking at the camera, crying, hand across his crotch, covered with paper money apparently tossed there by surrounding hands: "a tearful six-year-old boy is showered with lira and words of encouragement to prepare him for the Muslim rite of circumcision." Of course it would be ridiculously simplistic and reductionist to say that those who circumcise, *per se*, are more likely to make war. The old Romans, the Germans who marched to Hitler's tune, and the Japanese who terrorized Asia and attacked Pearl Harbor, for example, weren't circumcised. But genital mutilation is arguably a useful means (one of many) to desensitize a boy and socialize him into a social system in which war is seen to be good or necessary.

Dogma. In any thought system—from Judaism to Christianity to Marxism—it is the doctrinaire tendencies, not the liberational ones, that tend to become religious and political orthodoxy[45]; religious mandate of circumcision would seem to be no exception. In the short story "The Slaughterer" by Isaac Bashevis Singer, we learn about pious and gentle Yoineh Meir, who had expected to become his town's rabbi but instead is offered, and pressured into accepting, the lucrative and prestigious job of ritual slaughterer. He balks at the idea of making his living by killing, but a rabbi counsels him that it would be presumptuous to try to be "more compassionate than the Almighty, the Source of all compassion."

So Yoineh Meir reluctantly accepts, only to find that what he does to the animals, he feels himself. Their terror at their approaching death, their cries and screams as they die at his hands, the spurting and splattering of blood, the skinning of animals not yet completely dead, the all-pervasive suffering and stench of the place, come to haunt him more and more, day and night. Other people's bland acceptance of it all only adds alienation to his torment. Toward the end of the story, as the only way he can find out of his increasingly tortured state, out of the conflict between conscience and duty, he goes insane. As he does, he expresses a profound disillusionment (a casting off of illusions) that goes to the core of human liberation from social oppression:

> "I'll have none of your favors, God! I am no longer afraid of your Judgement! I am a betrayer of Israel, a wilful transgressor!" Yoineh Meir cried. "I have more compassion than God Almighty—more, more! He is a cruel God, a Man of War, a God of Vengeance. I will not serve Him. It is an abandoned world!" Yoineh Meir laughed, but tears ran down his cheeks in scalding drops.

> Yoineh Meir went to the pantry where he kept his knife, his whetstone, the circumcision knife. He gathered them all and dropped them into the pit of the outhouse. He knew that he was blaspheming, that he was desecrating the holy instruments, that he was mad, but he no longer wished to be sane.[46]

As essential as it is in the whole process of growth and enlightenment, such a reaction to oppression is only the starting point of the quest for sanity, for justice, for true spirituality, for personal and collective empowerment. To question authority is to move toward liberation; to live in reaction against it is to remain enslaved. If we can muster the courage to look honestly at our tendency to unquestioningly accept authority and tradition and, on the other hand, at our knee-jerk reactions against it, then we can begin to discover and move into the cleavage between these two forms of unmindfulness. From that space, with an open heart and mind, we can begin the process of inquiry and reevaluation essential to any life which seeks to be spiritual. From that space also comes non-reactive action for positive change and cultural evolution.

Even politically progressive, secular Jewish parents in the United States usually have their sons circumcised, though in doing so they often go through rationalizations that to the outside observer are quite astounding and convoluted. In Harry Brod's anthology *A Mensch Among Men: Explorations in Jewish Masculinity*, the brief chapter on circumcision by Zalman Schachter-Shalomi, a leading rabbi in the Jewish Renewal Movement, quotes such parents struggling with the conflict between protective parental instincts on the one hand and cultural expectations and religious authority on the other. Interestingly, all of the parents mentioned wind up going through with the circumcisions—no mention is made of those Jews in the United States and abroad who choose not to circumcise—and although a feminist critique is applied in other chapters on Jewish life and psychology, there is no analysis at all of circumcision beyond observing the sexist nature of the bris:

> What about our daughters? What ceremonial act initiates them into the Jewish Covenant with God? The fact is there is no Jewish female equivalent to a Bris (nor would any reasonable person suggest that a rite of excision be instituted). The roots of this

situation lie in the patriarchal past, where our heritage begins. Tradition, of course, carries great importance in the unfolding of our lives, but we must also be concerned with the present. Judaism is evolving, is attempting to meet the needs of real people here and now. The reality is that we must discover or allow for the revelation of a ritual for girls that will serve the convenautal function performed for boys by the Bris.[47]

The writer argues that no "reasonable person" would suggest cutting off part of the genitals of Jewish girls to solve the sexist dilemma of the bris, yet male circumcision is seen as an unalterable given. The humanistic observation that "Judaism is evolving" sits uncritically alongside an ethnocentric fundamentalism expressed elsewhere in the same chapter: "We have made a contract with God. He will be our God and we will be His people." The possibility (since "Judaism is evolving") of instituting a nonsurgical bris for both boys and girls is not even considered.

Cultural resistance. The tendency of the doctrinaire, ritualistic, and fundamentalist aspects of *any* belief system to predominate over a more fluid spirituality is strengthened in the face of external oppression. The retention of cultural practices then becomes an act of courage and resistance, of defiance against the forces of domination. Cultural forms which might otherwise come under internal criticism and gradually change and evolve are reinforced uncritically, for to change under threat is to give in to the oppressor. (Any form of bigotry or oppression has profound effects on the culture of the target/oppressed group in terms of gender roles, personal self-esteem, and group identification rituals.) And so Jewish ritual circumcision continued secretly under prohibitions against it during the Greek and Roman occupations of Israel and during the Spanish Inquisitions. These prohibitions were not motivated so much by concern for helpless infants, but rather by the desire to destroy or control Jewish culture or—in the erroneous belief that circumcision enhanced fertility—to limit the size of the Jewish population. We also have a more recent historical example of anti-circumcision measures not based in concern for the suffering of helpless babies: in the Nazi death camps, scenes of great brutality, circumcision was forbidden.

Jews throughout history have died rather than abandon this *mitzvah*,* and many feel that to give it up now—or even the surgical aspect of it—would be to dishonor their sacrifices. At the same time, and in apparent contradiction, many Jews also feel that their unique historic experience of suffering creates a special empathy with the victims of violence and oppression and an obligation to be as kind as possible to all people, all living things.

> The purpose of Jewish existence is not to eat Jewish food, or tell Jewish jokes, or use Yiddish words. It is to fight evil in the world. It is a source of deep pain to me to recognize how few people know this.
>
> —Dennis Prager and Rabbi Telushkin
> *The Nine Questions People Ask About Judaism*[48]

Holding uncritically to traditional forms helps a culture resist external oppression. Yet, as reactive behavior, it also tends to inhibit the expression of essential culture and true spirituality which are more open, more fluid. When one culture is abused by another, the result is not unlike that of an abused person— adaptive behaviors and attitudes are developed which help the person (or culture) survive but which, outside of the oppressive context, do not promote growth and happiness. To bring something to an illusion of completion, to a final inflexible form, is to have made it finite, and truth is anything but finite. This seems to be a basic flaw in any fundamentalist form of religion.

The historical impact of anti-Semitism strongly flavors Jewish response to cultural criticism even when benignly offered. It also poses serious questions about how Jews can raise the issue of ritual circumcision even among themselves.

> We're members of a Conservative congregation. I remember when we came here, hearing people talk in hushed tones: 'Did you know there's a move away from circumcision here in California?' People clicked their tongues in grave disapproval, and fear was in their voices: 'It's not good for us.' I, too, was shocked. Even now, after the difficult decision not to circumcise our son, we still haven't talked with our rabbi about it because we're afraid he might say he'd rather we weren't part of his congregation.[49]

---

* Leo Rosten, in *The Joys of Yiddish* (Pocket Books, Simon & Schuster, 1973), defines *mitzvah* variously as: "1. Commandment; divine commandment. 2. A meritorious act, one that expresses God's will; a 'good work,' a truly virtuous, kind, considerate, ethical deed." I like the latter definition.

GOY BOY / WRITING OF RITES

If it's difficult for Jews to question ritual circumcision, it's also difficult, in a different way, for a gentile. Especially a white, Anglo-Saxon Protestant like me who grew up in the Bible Belt, in an Ozark mountain poverty pocket of north Arkansas. When I walked down the aisle of our old brick church on a Sunday morning one summer long ago, I was followed by others "moved by the spirit." The day and time was set by the preacher, and in a country creek, in my best Sunday-go-to-meetin' clothes, I was baptized by immersion, soused under the water three times—"In the name of the Father!...and of the Son! ...and of the Holy Ghost!"—as my fellow church members, my beloved community, joyfully sang the old-time hymns on the rocky river bank. The memory is precious to me.

And so I grew up, small-town boy earning record attendance pins for Sunday school and church. Nary a Jew in sight. The verb "to jew (someone) down," meaning "to bargain down," we used unself-consciously, never considering that it might be offensive to someone; the more virulent forms of anti-Semitism ("Christ-killers!") I wasn't exposed to until later in life. To my young mind, Jews were biblical characters, along with Pharisees and Sadducees, who existed back in Jesus' time.

When I began this book, I knew I wanted to deal with ritual circumcision. I had been disturbed by the way the preservationist movement had not been able to do so, disturbed by statements like, "We're against circumcision *except as a religious rite*." This seemed to me profoundly dishonest. For if circumcision is what we say it is, and what I feel it in my very flesh to be, then it is so for everyone who experiences it—no matter what else it might be or however much it's suppressed, and underneath whatever validation there is for it in one's cultural group. Our bodies are our bodies. I was equally disturbed by the anti-Semitic anti-circumcision writings I had received in the mail after helping to found a group seeking to bring creative non-violent action into the preservationist movement. It reminded me of the white-supremacist literature of my southern childhood. There must be, I sensed, some sane and powerful alternative to the quick rationalization of ritual circumcision on the one hand and anti-Semitic tirades on the other.

I came to realize that, through my involvement in the non-violent direct action wings of other social movements, I'd had first-hand experience of a tradition that most active preservationists apparently hadn't, a tradition of bringing up and dealing directly with problems of sexism, racism, anti-Semitism, homophobia, or anything else within a movement that limits or oppresses its members or others outside it. Problems get talked about, and written about in nonviolence training manuals. It seemed to me that, if applied to the preservationist movement, such an approach could open up a space between bigotry and the complicity of silence, allowing for intelligent and heartful discussion of ritual circumcision. This sense—and my determination to follow it—has been strengthened by several things during the writing of this book.

First, people in the preservationist movement for the most part seemed not to share my perception that there's a big difference between taking an active stand against anti-Semitism and simply saying, "We're not anti-Semitic." At the end of the three-day First International Symposium on Circumcision (1989), I proposed to add to the drafted statement a specific declaration against "anti-Semitism and other forms of bigotry." After some debate, it passed, but the leadership chose—and to my knowledge continues to choose—to omit that part from the overall statement sent to the media. They do this not out of malice, but out of fear that if they even bring up the issues of ritual circumcision and anti-Semitism publicly, they'll wind up being accused of being anti-Semitic. In contrast, a number of friends and fellow activists in the peace and justice movements have understood almost immediately the importance of dealing upfront with both these interconnected and very emotional issues. This leads me to believe that the preservationist movement can learn and benefit from such an approach.

Second, in facilitating circumcision workshops, I've found Jewish men to be open to critical and intelligent reappraisal of ritual circumcision once they feel it's not just another cover for attacking Jews or Judaism. Of course, men who would come to a circumcision workshop are not by any means a cross section of society, Jewish or gentile. They are, by and large, men who have already undertaken to reevaluate a number of beliefs and attitudes. They are also among the ones able to see most clearly both the reality of circumcision and its social and political context. One man in particular comes to mind, from the workshop at the 1989 California Men's Gathering. Initially reserved, as if checking out the scene and the facilitators, he wound up telling a very interesting story. While living and traveling in Africa recently, he had witnessed a female circumcision ceremony and been disturbed by what he felt to be the obvious suffering of the young woman in contrast with the way the tribe was celebrating the event. Upon his return to the States, he was invited to his first bris (except for his own), and was struck by the parallel: relatives who had been shocked at hearing the female circumcision story were celebrating the cutting off of part of the baby's penis.

Third, the responses to my involvement in this issue by Jewish friends, colleagues, and acquaintances—mostly positive, some defensive, and quite a few a mixture of both—indicate to me that many Jews are undergoing an intensity of struggle over circumcision that's difficult for non-Jews to understand. (All except the most defensive have been curious, especially about the hidden history of preservationism within the Reform movement.) Many, especially expectant parents, feel they cannot speak freely of their feelings about circumcision in their own families and communities and feel relieved if they give birth to a girl. They feel torn between their cultural heritage (or family pressures) and their own parental instincts. Some suppress their feelings and have their sons circumcised; others yield to family pressures and then, when they see the reality of circumcision, regret it; while still others reject or drift away from the tradition which they feel puts them in such a bind, just as many used to feel forced to abandon Judaism in order to marry "outside the faith." One rabbi, who on request will perform a bris without a circumcision, told me that, just as Judaism has accommodated the reality of mixed marriages, with special programs to allow children to get the best of both parents' traditions, he expected that non-circumcision would come to be viewed as a definite option by most Jews within a few decades.[50]

On a personal level, I've chosen to write on ritual Jewish circumcision because it fascinates me and I wish to follow my interest and fascination. I hope that my doing so will help the preservationist movement break through the barrier of silence and contradiction in order to carry the struggle forward. Neo-Nazi groups, with anti-circumcision as part of their propaganda, pose a clear and present danger to the integrity of the movement through their potential to exploit preservationist sentiments for fascist ends. Especially non-Jews need to begin forming a viable preservationist alternative that deals directly and heartfully with the interrelated issues of ritual circumcision, patriarchy, and anti-Semitism.

Inter-tribal criticism is a tricky issue. (We all have various tribal identities, with one of the larger tribes being "American.") As a white southerner, I'm glad that outsiders presumed to challenge our practice of racial segregation, a practice most of us were unable or unwilling to criticize ourselves. Without "outsiders" as allies it is doubtful whether the descendents of former slaves would have been able to overturn legalized segregation alone. On the other hand, we don't want to judge another culture by the standards of our own and become like missionaries clothing the naked heathens. So how can we derive the benefits of cross-cultural criticism while minimizing the distortions and chances for abuse? I suggest that when anyone presumes to *constructively* criticize the practices of another tribe (not just use the issue to stir up hatred), it is helpful to follow what I call the

PRINCIPLES OF INTER-TRIBAL CRITICISM

1–Learn about historical and existing rivalries between your tribe and the one being criticized.

2–Learn about past and present disparities in the two tribes' relative political power as well as in their informal social clout.

3–Clearly define what it is about the practice that you don't like. (This prevents your objection to a particular practice from becoming a condemnation of the tribe as a whole.)

4–Voice your objections to members of the other tribe, and listen carefully to the responses. Ask questions without arguing.

5–Identify the various social and psychological needs that the objectionable practice serves for members of the other tribe. Consider other ways in which these needs might be met. (Needs may well be different for different members of the tribe, and the needs of some may conflict with those of others: male vs. female, leaders and the powerful vs. commoners, rich vs. poor, adults vs. children, and so on.)

6–Find out what fears might underlie both the practice in question and any resistance to reevaluating it. Think about ways in which you and your tribe could alleviate those fears.

7–Develop positive personal, political, and/or working relationships with members of the tribe, and find ways to celebrate those aspects of their culture that you like.

8–List the unsavory aspects of your own tribe's history and current practices, both in general and, especially, in relation to the other tribe. Be willing to readily and fully acknowledge these things. (In terms of credibility, it is helpful also to have a personal history of speaking out and acting against the unsavory aspects of your own tribe before pontificating about another tribe's shortcomings.)

9–Be open to the possibility that you may just possibly be wrong, or that you may not have fully understood the context in which the practice occurs.

Ritual circumcision is clearly cultural, and criticism of it is a cross-cultural criticism, no matter how much we try to avoid the issue by saying we're opposed to circumcision "except as a religious rite." While circumcision has become a cultural phenomenon for gentiles, too—despite the medical reasons given, which Jews also usually give—it's much more deeply enculturated for Jews. It embodies the very essence of how we human beings can evolve, adopt, or have imposed a violent, limiting, or oppressive custom and over time come to view it as normal, perpetuated and even idealized in the way that the Chinese used to idealize bound feet. I suspect that, to the extent that we can understand Jewish circumcision, we can gain insight into how the rest of us enculturate the practice—as well as how we've wound up with a number of other social, ecological, political, and military practices in need of change. Following these Principles of Inter-Tribal Criticism, we can build bridges, dissolve fear, allow each of our various tribes to transcend a parochial view, and learn a good deal from each other.

AVOIDANCE AND CONNECTIONS

The preservationist movement's resistance to dealing with ritual circumcision has probably been wise, considering that it has not really dealt with anti-Semitism and how anti-Semitic campaigns and groups have exploited preservationist sentiments. At the First International Symposium on Circumcision, there were no presentations or discussions that dealt specifically with anti-Semitism. (There was, though, a talk by well-known mohel Joel Shoulson in which he said of Jewish circumcision, "What we're talking about here is fundamentalism."[51]). As mentioned above, both gentiles and Jews in the movement have assumed that to avoid being smeared with the tar of anti- Semitism—and simply because circumcision is too embedded in Jewish culture and theology to yield to direct criticism—one must remain silent on ritual circumcision. And so we hear those hedged statements condemning circumcision "except as a religious rite," leading some Jewish men to feel not only victimized by their tradition but abandoned by the preservationist movement.

> So much is being done today to educate the public about medical circumcision. However, I see that most of those writing about medical circumcision refuse to discuss religious circumcision. Well, I am 28 years old and have a very unsatisfactory sex life because I lost over half of my glans during a ritual circumcision. Aren't Jewish babies entitled to a foreskin as well? What is really anti-Semitic is the refusal to acknowledge that the same rights that non-Jewish babies have should be accorded to Jewish babies as well.[52]

The false dichotomy of silence vs. anti-Semitism can be transcended only by those who are opposed to routine circumcision, especially gentiles, getting and putting out the message clearly: anti-Semitism reinforces ritual circumcision and therefore circumcision generally. There are neo-Nazi groups that latch onto circumcision as an excuse to trash Jews. One extreme piece of propaganda from such a group combines a few perfectly valid arguments against circumcision with the claim that it causes homosexuality and that

> It is unworthy of the advanced White Race to accept such a barbaric practice, just as it is to accept nigger music, nigger and/or Jewish practices, mores, and religions.[53]

In the face of such attitudes—whether expressed simple-mindedly or with more reserve—it seems to me important to deal in an up-front manner with anti-Semitism in ourselves, in the preservationist movement, and in the larger society. To do otherwise is to impede the advent of an intact world—in every sense of the term. One active preservationist I've met, a generous, soft-spoken Bible Belt minister, founded his own organization (Remain Intact) and has helped a number of people come to terms with their and their children's disabilities caused by circumcision. Politically naive and anxious to get out the preservationist word, he is quite happy that his anti-circumcision (and often anti-Jewish) writings are incorporated into the literature of such neo-Nazi groups as the New Order on his mailing list.

The movement has not dealt very well with this dangerous weak flank and has not developed much of a response beyond embarassed silence. Its activists seem to understand well that simply to say "I'm not anti-Semitic" is about as convincing as, "Some of my best friends are Negroes." Even if true, such statements sound suspiciously like a cover for prejudice. Like Richard Nixon proclaiming "I am not a crook," it draws suspicion: "If you're not," the listener may ask, "why are you going to the trouble to deny it?" On the other hand, what seems not very well understood is the difference between denying anti-Semitism and dealing directly and honestly with it inside and outside the movement. To face and admit our own biases and deal openly with the reasons behind them while clearly denouncing bigotry and backing up our words with action when the Klan marches, Nazis dominate the news, or we receive anti-Semitic anti-circumcision literature—this leaves no room for the expression of hidden racist agendas. It opens an alternative to silence versus anti-Semitic tirades, which for too long have been the two unsatisfactory responses to Jewish ritual circumcision. It allows us to see that ritual circumcision is not so much Jewish as it is patriarchal and fundamentalist (and reinforced by anti-Semitism). Though the history of anti-Semitism dictates that it must be Jews who lead the fight against Jewish circumcision, the quality of gentiles' solidarity in that struggle—and whether it helps or hinders the fight—will depend on the extent to which we are willing to confront anti-Semitism in ourselves and others.

GUILT & RESPONSIBILITY

"Confront" is a heavy-sounding word, but in taking a stand against bigotry, we need not become self-righteous, nor distort those with prejudiced attitudes in the same way they distort others. We/they are not bad people for having prejudical attitudes learned from others. I have yet to meet anyone who is not prejudiced in some form or another (though it's hard for each of us to see our own biases). In fact, what we call prejudice is often just misinformation, or even correct information taken out of context and blown out of proportion—as a person pained over their own circumcision (or appreciative of their foreskin) might view Jews as "barbaric" because they circumcise, ignoring the many positive aspects of the culture. This incomplete or distorted view of another group then gets amplified by frustrations in other areas of our lives—my boss gives me a bad time so I go to the bar, get drunk, and grumble about not only my boss but Mexicans, Jews, women, "niggers," "queers," or "bums" on the street. We all inherit this stuff (in gross or subtle form) from others, from our family, friends, and society, and it's fueled by our own limitations and hurts. We're not to blame for it; it's not our *fault*. It doesn't mean we're bad. We are, however, *responsible* for how we deal with it, what we do with it—there's a big difference between fault and responsibility. We have a choice: we can continue in our unthinking patterns, or we can discuss our attitudes and behavior openly, exploring the implications and alternatives.

Whether we're talking about circumcision or bigotry, it's essential to find out how we got to where we are and to understand the historical factors behind any cultural behavior. To the extent that we do so, we can stop being slaves of the past and of the powers that be. We can explore alternative ways to achieve whatever positive functions are now served by otherwise destructive behaviors. (A fundamental principle of social and cultural change is that for any institution or practice we wish to change, we must identify whatever positive functions it serves in order to find alternative ways to serve those needs.) We *do* have options. It's up to each of us to choose how we manifest our spirituality, in which ways we express and evolve our cultural identity. The responsibility of choice is inescapable. Even if we unquestioningly follow tradition and authority, we are *choosing* to do so. In this age of nuclear overkill and ecological crisis, a serious reevaluation of our ways of thinking and acting would seem to be in order. Whatever serves to create a viable, gentle, and humane future can be embraced and nurtured. That which does not contribute in this way we can leave rapidly and respectfully behind.

After leaving my cultural womb and involving myself in the government's War on Poverty and later the anti-Vietnam War movement, I gradually came to notice that there was a disproportionate number of Jews among my fellow activists, as has been the case in other social change groups I've been involved in since that time. In his introduction to *A Mensch Among Men: Explorations in Jewish Masculinity*, Harry Brod recounts some of the reasons commonly given for this disproportionality: "elements of Jewish culture such as its commitments to justice and equality, its messianism, and its emphasis on intellectualism and ideas, and other more sociological factors, such as the particular marginality of Jews, the economic and social roots of anti-Semitism, and a historical sympathy for the underdog." So on the issue of circumcision it is not surprising that some of the most dedicated preservationists are Jewish men like Edward Wallerstein, author of *Circumcision: An American Health Fallacy*, a major medical work on the subject; Dean Edell, M.D., a nationally syndicated radio and TV medical advisor; publisher Ralph Ginzburg, veteran of free speech battles and Director of O.U.C.H., Inc. (Outlaw Unnecessary Circumcision in Hospitals) in New York; and activists like the following:

> As a Jewish boy, I was circumcised at a religious ceremony. I first found out from some older woman who once gushed, "Look how big you've grown. I remember you at your bris (the ceremony)!" That's when I found out not only about circumcision, but that they actually had a party to celebrate, and that strangers were present to watch. I felt a tremendous sense of violation.
>
> I get angry when I hear it classified as elective surgery. From the point of view of the victim, it is no more "elective" than the surgery that Dr. Mengele "elected" to perform on concentration camp inmates.[54]

While it may be tempting to dismiss this statement as trivializing the victims of the Holocaust—or as an example of internalized anti-Semitism—to dismiss it would be to trivialize this man's feelings. The reference to "elective" surgery goes directly to the core of the issues of infant rights and informed consent, and the whole statement is, if anything, a rebellion against trivialization of male genital mutilation.

MASKS AND MIRRORS

Language often reveals more about ourselves than we intend and our choice of words can show the way we humans idealize things that we might otherwise see in a different light. The stunted, deformed feet that resulted from foot-binding of Chinese girls were called "Golden Lotuses"[55] and were considered highly attractive and desirable. Their counterpart—normal feet—were seen as gross and ugly. Similarly, *The Layman's Guide to the Covenant of Circumcision* calls circumcision the "Golden Circle,"[56] while in one article on circumcision which I read, a rabbi writing of his own struggle between protective parental instinct and the cultural mandate to circumcise his newborn son refers to the intact penis with its foreskin as "a stopped-up dullness." (In the end, this man resolved to go through with it despite his misgivings, and even to perform the circumcision himself, as the Moslem physician was prepared to do to her daughter—see pages 29–30.)

The *Encyclopedia Judaica* says that, unlike the genital mutilations practiced by surrounding heathen tribes, Jewish circumcision "sanctified the human body and aided it in its fight against erotic indulgence..."[57]

CHALLENGE AND CHANGE

The Jewish Reform Movement started out in the early 1800s as a lay movement—ordinary people taking charge of their social and spiritual heritage. A wide variety of obligations under Talmudic law were reevaluated, changed, or simply dropped. Synagogues became temples, dietary laws went out, services were conducted in the national language instead of Hebrew, and so on. Few Jews today have any inkling that for quite a number of years circumcision was stopped altogether by the early Reform movement. Then, with the increasing influence of rabbis who started to take notice of this growing lay movement and become involved in it, many of the initial changes—including the abolition of circumcision—were reversed.[58] Circumcision was not reinstituted without a battle, however. Writings and speeches were often scathing in their condemnation of the practice. Felix Adler, Columbia University philosophy professor, former rabbinical student, founder-to-be of the Ethical Culture movement, and son of a leading Reform rabbi, Samuel Adler, viewed circumcision as "simply barbarous in itself and utterly barbarous and contemptible in its origin."[59]

The preservationists eventually lost the battle to an increasingly conservative Reform leadership and as a result, circumcision is practiced by most Reform Jews in the United States today. It's usually done in a hospital, though, with a naming ceremony performed separately later. (While all circumcisions are violent and cruel, those performed in hospitals are arguably more traumatic because of the impersonal surroundings and the longer time taken.) As a result, an intact baby boy can now be taken to a Reform synagogue where the naming ceremony will be conducted with the assumption that the circumcision has already taken place. There might even be a rabbi sympathetic to parental reservations about circumcision, though the best chances are probably with a *havurah* (informal meeting group) rabbi with no official congregation. He (or she) has less at stake and would be more likely to go along with such a controversial request. Official naming certificates are available from the Society for Humanistic Judaism (see Appendix A). I was quite surprised when, at one synagogue I visited, the office manager compared the clitoridectomies done on girls in other cultures with male circumcision. "I guess you can tell where I stand on this," she said. "It's genital mutilation."

YESH G'VUL

Of course, such attitudes can be discounted by the more religiously orthodox as the corrupting influence of secular humanism. One Jewish man came up to me at an outreach table I was staffing at a university, dismissed humanistic strains in Judaism as fleeting aberrations in the vast panorama of history, and justified circumcision because it was a practice of great antiquity. I pointed out that many Moslems circumcised both boys and girls, and asked, "If tradition and scriptures said to circumcise your daughters, would you do it?" "No, of course not," he said. "There are limits."

"Yesh G'vul," "there are limits," is the rallying cry—and the name—of the peace movement among Israeli soldiers shocked by their government's actions against the *intifada*, the Palestinian uprising. We all have limits beyond which we will not (or should not) go, even under orders of respected authority or in pursuit of what we consider laudable ends. In terms of circumcision, what the preservationist movement is doing is re-drawing the line, the limit, not in a sexist manner between boys and girls, but humanely between helpless babies and legal adults able to make informed choices about their own bodies. (One of the fall-back proposals in the Reform movement as circumcision was being reinstituted was to make it an adult procedure done of free choice, perhaps with only a small portion of the foreskin removed; unfortunately, it failed. The only progress made that didn't get reversed was elimination of the circumcision requirement for adult converts to Judaism.)

The issue of circumcision can seem beguilingly simple—"If it ain't broke, don't fix it!"—but for Jews its roots go as far back as patriarchy itself, and as deep as the collective trauma of genocide. When we speak of the pain and loss of circumcision, what many Jews hear is not our compassion or logic, but historical echoes of pogroms, of evictions from ancestral lands, of shattered glass and dreams, of the rap on the door before being taken away. The seige mentality—circling the wagon train under attack—that has been created by historical anti-Semitism has made cooperation difficult between Jews and gentiles with common preservationist aims; Jews working with gentiles in the movement are often viewed as "consorting with the enemy."

So the challenge raised by the preservationist movement is far more profound and difficult for Jews than the mere century-old medical arguments and the parental insecurities that gentiles have to deal with. For some reason this seems especially true for Jews in the United States. The Summer 1988 issue of the journal *Humanistic Judaism* carried an article titled "A Mother Questions *Brit Milla"*:

> Coming from a European background where routine circumcisions as practiced in most American hospitals are nonexistent, and where many Jews reject a brit milla as an archaic and barbaric ritual, I simply assumed that the [American] Jewish community had

divergent approaches to this issue just as with every other aspect of Judaism. I was stunned to realize that questioning this ritual is the ultimate taboo among American Jews. Not only was I not supposed to question it, but I was not even supposed to have the feelings and concerns that I had....Anyone who dares to question the brit milla ritual is angrily silenced, laughed at, lightly dismissed, or labelled "a traitor undermining Judaism"...[60]

But change is in the air. Feminist Jewish women in Israel have now carried the Torah to the Wailing Wall and led prayers there, outraging Orthodox rabbis who seek to preserve unquestioningly the old patriarchal ways. ("A woman carrying a Torah," the *New York Times* quoted the Orthodox rabbi in charge of the area as saying, "is like a pig at the Wailing Wall."[61]) The Alternative Bris Support Group is helping the small but growing number of parents who choose not to circumcise while still raising their children as cultural or even religious Jews. As the Us/Them, Jew/gentile divide softens (a process impeded by anti-Semitism), deep internal value differences between fundamentalist and humanistic Jews emerge. Suppressed to the extent that the community as a whole feels the need for a forced unity in the face of external threats, these differences are becoming more and more apparent on a variety of issues, most dramatically in relation to the policies of Israel in the Palestinian uprising. Already we're beginning to see a sort of preservationist version of liberation theology, as some rabbinical students and even rabbis question circumcision, following the lead of lay people.

When followers take the lead, leaders will eventually follow. It seems only a matter of time until Jewish men, a courageous few at first, pick up on and carry forward last century's preservationist movement within Reform Judaism by applying the politics of modern nonviolent protest. If women could torch bras to protest their restrictions and if draft cards could be burned to express our agony over the napalming of Vietnamese villages, then bris certificates could certainly be sliced up or drenched in blood to point out the contradiction of having ritual genital mutilation in what is otherwise a joyous occasion.

Personal Change and Political Action

THE LOSS

Despite the identification of infant male circumcision with Judaism, in the United States, where less than 3% of the population is Jewish, circumcision is overwhelmingly a secular, not a religious, phenomenon. Or, more accurately, it's an issue for all men in this country. As men, we pay a dear price for our dubious privileges in this society. Our sensitivities are—must be—assaulted, limited, denied, in order for the warring industrial system to work. We are socialized into being cannon fodder and killers for our various countries, as well as money and success objects working ourselves to an early death. We are ridiculed into denying our softer, more nurturing sides. In the United States, most of us are welcomed into life by having part of our penises cut off, followed by days of sometimes intense burning as urine and feces irritate the exposed, raw glans and unhealed surgical wound. I can now remember my post-surgery wailing, the pain of my loss, age six: "Oh, my penis! Oh, my penis!" My cries, wave after wave of hurt and pain, filled the corridors of the entire small-town hospital. And I was relatively lucky, mind you: because of being past infancy, I'd had the benefit of general anesthesia during the surgery itself. My foreskin, prematurely pulled back as doctors frequently and ignorantly do or advise parents to do (see pages 18–19), had developed lesions to the glans in a way that caused pain in urination. A circumcision was recommended to solve the problem once and for all. My mother says that hearing me was heart-rending. "You thought you were ruined, for sure!" she now recalls, laughing.

Ruined? No. Unlike some circumcision victims, I'm sexually functional, at least to the extent that a foreskinless man can be.

Robbed, violated, assaulted, ripped off? Most certainly, and the more I learn, the more ripped off I feel.

It's not easy to hear a lover say that she prefers intact men, although I know that, other factors being equal (they never are, of course), I would prefer an intact woman over a circumcised one for a lover. It's not easy to accept that I've lost what would have been additional pleasure, both for me and for a partner. It's not easy to read this letter from a man circumcised as an adult:

> The acute sensitivity never returned; something rather precious to a sensual hedonist had been lost forever....[C]ircumcision destroys a very joyful aspect of the human experience for both males and females.[62]

There are complex psychological factors at work with the loss of such erotic tissue as a foreskin and frenulum and the resultant decrease in sensitivity of the glans. (In general, circumcision's desensitizing effect becomes more pronounced as a man grows older, and is more likely to lead to problems in achieving orgasm.) Although adult circumcision is far less traumatic than infant circumcision—it's done *with* anesthesia, *with* the patient's consent, *with* a perceived benefit, and *without* ripping apart the foreskin and glans which are normally fused together in infancy—our best source of information on how circumcision affects sexuality is reports from men circumcised in adulthood. Some report a short-term *increase* in sensitivity before desensitization sets in within a few weeks, months, or, in rare cases, years. Some are happy with their circumcision because it relieved them from some medical condition that had been afflicting them—they usually don't know that their problem might well have been remedied with less drastic measures by a doctor who valued and understood foreskins. Others say they like the lessened sensitivity because it gives them "more control" over ejaculation. "Control" can be an important consideration to a man taught that he must *perform* and who hasn't learned to relax into and play with a sexual partner. (It has also been suggested that there's a strong need among men circumcised in adulthood to justify their post-operative state by focusing on real or imagined positive aspects.) A considerable number of circumcised men, however, are less than happy with their condition. Their feelings range from disappointment to depression to intense rage (see Appendix E). Some have a mix of feelings. One man in his late 50s wrote to a medical advice column that he had had "a much needed circumcision" (why it was needed he didn't say), but that now "I cannot get an erection to have a normal sex life."[63] All too typically, the doctor told him the circumcision probably had nothing to do with it, and advised him to explore other causes.

At the First International Symposium on Circumcision, one speaker, who had been circumcised in adulthood, described the difference between pre- and post-operative sexual sensation as "subtle," akin to seeing in color compared to black and white: the function remains (seeing, feeling), but certain sensory input simply isn't there anymore. Other men report much more dramatic differences in sensation. One who I talked with underwent surgical foreskin restoration to regain sensitivity of the glans and with it the ability to orgasm. He noted a world of difference in sensitivity and pleasure with and without a foreskin. Having experienced ridicule in his long search for a competent and sympathetic surgeon, he compared the psychological implications of foreskin loss with what a woman experiences after a mastectomy. "No one today would tell a woman she shouldn't be emotionally traumatized by the loss of part of her body," he says. "It's a natural reaction. So how *dare* they tell me I shouldn't mourn my loss and want my foreskin back?" (See Appendix B for a method of nonsurgical foreskin restoration and names of doctors who do surgical restorations.)

Some men, upon realizing what's been done to them by circumcision (some have carried this knowledge all along), fall into a deep remorse. Such mourning is natural, as is the reaction to any loss. A few, though, seem to stay there indefinitely. Activists in the preservationist movement can tell about any number of cases of men locked for years into their pain. Franklin Abbott, psychotherapist and author of *New Men, New Minds: Breaking Male Tradition*, talks about coping with loss:

> Loss and the inability to make it up or make it right can be more frightening than death itself. It can also be a portal to a deeper understanding of self and an invitation to a more radical aliveness. We are challenged by the loss to believe it, to grieve it and to let go of what was true before the loss occurred in order to live authentically in the present...

> We do not always choose our losses but we can choose to respond to them bringing to bear our intelligence, intuition and compassion....On the other side of grief are new possibilities, greater wisdom and deeper loving self-acceptance. In nature fires are necessary to keep forests and swamps vital ecosystems. Though it may not be your lightening that has ignited the fire that created the loss, how you live with it, day by day, hour by hour, is largely up to you.[64]

My own circumcision happened after infancy. My parents never even considered having it done when I was born, for which I'm grateful. They did what what they felt was best for me. It was only because of what seemed to be medical necessity that they later consented, and my mother now regrets not exploring alternatives.

> At times my conscience bothers me about having you circumcised. It seemed right at the time to do as the doctor encouraged. I knew so little about it...I can see so many ways I'd do differently now.

With busy, hectic lives, ill-informed and misinformed by trusted medical experts, it's understandable how parents can make a decision to circumcise. But once we know about the risks of circumision and the trauma hidden behind hospital doors, once we know of the sexual price paid, we can stop doing it.

GETTING IT BACK—FORESKIN RESTORATION

Like the great majority of men my age in the United States—including doctors who circumcise and judges who preside over legal challenges to the practice—I don't really know what I'm missing. I can't. Gone forever are my former foreskin's millions of cells, several yards of nerves, fifty nerve endings, a hundred sweat glands, and several feet of blood vessels.[65] Gone is my penis's own natural "personal lubrication." And, adding irritation to injury, my partly desensitized, constantly exposed glans is still much more easily irritated than a foreskin is by rubbing against clothes.

All, however, is not lost. While the skin, nerves, and blood vessels of my former foreskin (and frenulum) are gone forever, it *is* possible to once again have a foreskin. How? There are two ways to re-cover the glans bared by circumcision: surgery and the stretching of remaining skin. Both these techniques are ancient but with modern improvements. Surgery is far quicker, with immediate results (after a short period of recuperation). It's expensive, though insurance companies sometimes pay. It's also riskier—you may wind up with an inadequate or botched restoration job and be worse off than before. The one man I've met who had undergone surgical restoration had spent some time with stretching techniques with good results, but was impatient for full restoration. He spent a lot of time researching the subject, finding doctors who would do it (there are very few), and interviewing both the doctors and their former patients— which anyone should do before embarking on the procedure. This man's job took him all over the country, making the interviews easy to schedule. He's so happy with the results that he can hardly stop talking about his increased pleasure and newfound sense of wholeness. Even he, however, recommends that men first try stretching techniques before considering surgery, and that surgery not be unertaken without thorough research and interviews of doctors and their former patients.

Stretching is another matter, and is based on a simple principle. According to *Foreskin Restoration (Uncircumcision)* (Appendix A), when any skin is stretched, the stretching causes microscopic tears between the skin cells. If the stretched skin is released, as is usually the case, these heal back as before. If, however, the stretching is constant—as when a person gains weight—the body manufactures new cells to fill in between the separated ones. This results in new skin. This principle is the basis for foreskin restoration through skin stretching. The most common techniques involve stretching the remaining foreskin (or, if there isn't any, the penis's shaft skin) and taping it in the stretched position. (See Appendix B.) Circumcised men with some remaining foreskin will be able to get a new foreskin in less time than required by men with "tight" circumcisions in which all possible skin was cut off.

Still, it's not quick. The time usually required is two to four years of fairly consistent stretching—depending on the amount of skin left, the elasticity of that skin, how consistent you are in stretching, whether you leave the stretching device on at night, and so on. I've been using a taping technique for a nmber of months now. While I haven't been as consistent as I could be, I've been surprised by the increased softness and sense of wholeness I get from my glans being covered by natural skin, something I'd lived my whole adult life without knowing. This feeling is reinforced by reports from men who have accomplished their restorations, so that the considerable hassle of "taping up" most mornings seems well worth it. At a workshop that I helped facilitate, one of the other facilitators had been doing restorational stretching for some time. I had not met him before, though we had talked on the phone. As the workshop ended, we announced that this facilitator had agreed to show us the results of his foreskin stretching for those with sufficient interest to stay a few more minutes. Needless to say, he stole the show. Nobody left, and everyone—myself included—was astounded at the full foreskin this man had achieved through a simple stretching technique he had developed himself. (Contact NOCIRC, Appendix A, for information on his technique).

Foreskin restoration support groups have now started to form to help men through this process (see Appendix A).

COMING OUT: THE HEALING BEGINS

Doctors debate the issue endlessly, just as the arguments went on and on in my native South about whether blacks had the same mental capacity as whites and whether segregated black schools were as good as the white schools. While it was necessary to engage in such debates in order to expose the lies that supported institutionalized oppression, it was black people (and white allies) finally standing up (and marching and sitting-in) and saying "No more!" that sent Jim Crow reeling. It was Stonewall that launched gay rights into the political agenda, and street demonstrations, draft card burnings, and the choice of jail over genocide that helped extract us from Vietnam.

Action, in short, speaks louder than words. Those of us victimized in various ways and to varying degrees by circumcision have a unique power to make parents understand that it's not just an academic debate, that their own sons may well come to resent having their genitals mutilated, regardless of the parents' motivation in having it done. (See Appendix E.) Some are beginning to translate their pain and anger into desire for political action beyond the educational and lobbying work already being done.

(T)he greatest disadvantage of circumcision, in my view, is the awful loss of sensitivity when the foreskin is removed....I was deprived of my foreskin when I was 26; I had had ample experience in the sexual area, and I was quite happy (delirious, in fact) with what pleasure I could experience—beginning with foreplay and continuing—as an intact male. After my circumcision, that pleasure was utterly gone. Let me put it this way: on a scale of 10, the uncircumcised penis experiences pleasure that is at least 11 or 12; the circumcised penis is lucky to get to 3. Really—and I mean this in all seriousness—if American men who were circumcised at birth could know the deprivation of pleasure that they would experience, they would storm the hospitals and not permit their sons to undergo this unnecessary loss.[66]

"Storming the hospitals" is the idea behind The Victims Speak, founded in 1988 with the following principles and goals:

Nonviolence. [We seek] to bring the principles and techniques of nonviolent action...into the [preservationist] movement, giving creative voice to the victims of circumcision.

Culture. We view circumcision as...a cultural phenomena, whether practiced with a medical or a religious rationale and whether performed on infants or adolescents, males or females.

Anti-Semitism. We seek to deal directly with...anti-Semitism, both historically and now—within ourselves, within the [preservationist] movement, and in society at large...

Abolition. We seek the end of all forms of involuntary genital mutilation for whatever reason. We believe that each person has a fundamental right to a gentle infancy, an intact body, and full adult sexuality regardless of race, gender, or parents' belief system.

Unity. We are feminist...*and* we embrace men's rights, seeing no inherent contradiction....We support cultural diversity and those aspects of any philosophy or belief system which unite us in caring relationship to each other and to our bleeding planet.[67]

WHAT'S LEFT?

The task of breaking through public ignorance, habit, and vested interests has so far fallen to a relative few individuals and groups deeply committed to this one issue. They pressure hospitals to really inform expectant parents before they sign the consent form for circumcision, they press insurance companies to stop paying for non-therapeutic circumcisions, they educate expectant parents, they work for change within their professional organizations, and so on. The National Organization of Circumcision Information Resource Centers(NOCIRC) is the clearinghouse for such activism. It's executive director, Marilyn Fayre Milos, R.N., is mother of three circumcised boys and grandmother of one intact child—"We're learning!" she says, laughing, but with a hint of sadness in her voice. When she's asked about her sons' circumcisions, the sadness comes to the surface. Like many parents, she didn't know any better; she thought it was the best thing to do, that the doctor knew best.

Milos was launched into this cause when, after her children were grown, she decided to become a nurse-midwife. In nursing school she witnessed a circumcision for the first time and was deeply shocked by it (see Appendix D). When she was fired from her hospital for informing parents about the risks of circumcision, she and others founded the non-profit educational organization Informed Consent, later to become NOCIRC. Milos is frequently a guest on TV and radio shows around the country. Her regional nurses' association has awarded her its highest award for Clinical Excellence in Perinatal Nursing for "almost single-handedly rais[ing] public consciousness about America's most unnecessary surgery" and for her "dedication and unwavering commitment to 'righting a wrong'..."[68] While there are other preservationist organizations and individuals doing valuable independent work (see Appendix A), most activism currently is in affiliation with NOCIRC.

Like a number of other new social movements—Green, feminist, gay rights, animal liberation—the preservationist cause has formed outside the traditional political left. It's also essentially ignored by it. Even books dealing extensively with female circumcision abroad, books like Mary Daly's *Gyn Ecology: The Metaphysics of Radical Feminism*, usually somehow avoid any mention of the routine genital mutilation of male babies in the United States. This brings up serious questions of analysis and cultural bias. While the focus of such books is quite properly on female circumcision, are we to assume that the violent and patriarchal nature of infant male circumcision and the overriding of protective parental instinct by the demands of a male medical or religious priesthood are irrelevant to women's oppression? On another level, are we to believe that more severe forms or degrees of violation are sufficient reason to ignore lesser forms or degrees? If so, are we then to believe that the existance of rape is a valid reason to ignore mugging, murder to ignore rape, and genocide to ignore discrimination? I fail to see the logic that the usually greater degree of mutilation of female children in other cultures somehow makes it o.k. to less severely mutilate the genitals of male children in our own. Some women (including some feminists), when presented with real emotions and rational arguments against infant male circumcision, react with something like, "Oh, my God, there go those men talking about their penises again—can't they think of anything else?" thereby trivializing and discounting our personal feelings, experience, and concerns just as men so frequently do to women. While such attitudes are understandable in light of so much of women's experience with men, nonetheless they prevent the forging of a common front against the various violations that we experience.

To my knowledge, the right of baby boys (and therefore adult men) to intact genitals and full and natural sexuality has not been endorsed by any groups defining themselves as either liberal or progressive. Why? For one thing, their members are as indoctrinated as the rest of us into accepting male circumcision as normal. The idea of a man's right to intact genitals seems to many of them foreign and ridiculous—though they would presumably (I hope) rise in stormy protest if female circumcision were proposed for either "medical" or "religious" reasons. Perhaps they also fear that criticism of circumcision would be perceived as anti-Semitic and thereby be divisive within their organizations. (As mentioned previously, some neo-Nazis have incorporated preservationist sentiments into their racist and anti-Semitic literature, as both the left and responsible conservatives stand silently by.) A sad comment on the political left was made at the First International Symposium on Circumcision. One speaker from Islamic Africa, when asked what the revolutionary movements' positions were on the various female and male genital mutilations common there, replied that because they were fighting for "political," not "cultural," change, they took no stand.[69] In terms of male genital mutilation—which can be seen as fascism quite literally embodied—the same can be said for every single labor, liberal, or left group in the United States. A major alternative publisher of books on peace, justice, and nonviolent social change wouldn't even consider publishing the book you hold in your hands (back when it was just an idea) because the subject was too much "on the fringe." I wonder: in this age of glasnost and perestroika, will our bodies, our *genitals*, be exempt by a calcified left so locked into its traditional agenda and so concerned with being "acceptable" to its established constituency that it can't see new horizons? Or will we see an opening of minds and hearts, a restructuring of the way we view culture, our bodies, and sexuality? "Glasnost" means "opening," but it also means "speaking out," which the preservationist movement—and virtually no one on the left—is doing about genital mutilation in the United States.

Like green/ecology concerns, the preservationist movement is "neither right nor left." It tries to bring out the best of both "progressives" and "conservatives." It seeks to liberate us from socially-entrenched violence and oppression, *and* it seeks to preserve (to conserve) that which is good and natural from unwarranted meddling and destruction.

> It is not easy to see evil in something that has the sanction of long tradition, but traditions can be bad as well as good. They represent inherited error as well as inherited truth, and it is the reformer's job to tackle and clear away whatever is harmful in them.
>
> —Archbishop Lang (UK)[70]

BREAKING SILENCE—HEALING THE PATRIARCHAL WOUND

Silence as a respite from the incessant chatter of the outside world and of our minds is a beautiful thing. Silence about things that need to be said is quite another, reinforcing old ways and inhibiting the advent of better ways of thinking and being. Our cultural silence about circumcision is of the latter sort. Workshops on "Breaking Silence: Circumcision as Genital Mutilation: Healing the Patriarchal Wound" are organized by The Victims Speak. The group also refers people to other workshops and to written materials and resource people dealing with strategizing nonviolent social change; unlearning racism, sexism, and anti-Semitism; getting in touch with repressed feelings in order to work through them in a way that leads to empowerment through social action; and nonviolence trainings for direct action. Men are encouraged to try the variety of sustained gentle stretching techniques for foreskin restoration as well as (carefully) to check out surgical options. In doing this, we not only start to regain a lost sense of wholeness, a moistness, and greater sensitivity; we also make a powerful political and cultural statement. The genital mutilation industry is able to continue because its infant victims are powerless to non-cooperate and because we adults passively and silently accept the consequences of what's been done to us. Breaking that silence is a major step toward abolition, and doing what we can to get back what was taken away from us is an important part of breaking that silence.

Organizing around the issue of circumcision is difficult, because few men consciously have any idea of what's been done to them. Those who do know are understandably reluctant to acknowledge their violation and their loss even among friends, much less to stand up in public and declare it. One man recently asked to be removed from a contact list for preservationist actions because "It's too painful for me to be reminded of circumcision in any way." While he is, sadly, incapacitated by his pain, at least this man is aware of his trauma. There are many more men circumcised as infants who are in a state of profound denial reinforced by a lack of information.

Awareness about circumcision seems much higher among gay and bisexual men, probably because they experience other men's penises and can compare. Most of us heterosexual men never get that opportunity—we're too afraid of being called "queer" to look at or ask about, much less feel, other men's genitals. And so we muddle through our sex lives not knowing what we're missing, with no idea that it could ever be better, that we've been ripped off. Had I not met and become friends with an active preservationist, I would have stayed like the overwhelming majority of people in the United States—uninformed or in denial.

As others helped me become aware, this book, if it accomplishes what I want it to accomplish, will cause other men to go through what I've gone through and continue to go through in facing and accepting my own genital mutilation.

I was circumcised when I was eight days old. When making love I never thought about my circumcised state. It was...normal for me. Now that I have read the prerelease version of your book, I'm not relaxed about it anymore. You've made me conscious about a mutilation I did not want, but was unable to stop.

After the book I could not make love like I used to. I shall have to accept the mutilation first, and get the same acceptance from my girlfriend....It feels like people who don't want to know about battery [factory-farmed] chicken in order to eat their meat in peace. In the same way I'm not sure if I like being circumcision-conscious.

....If God created us in His image, then why should we try to improve on this by mutilating that image?...[L]ove and a lot of thanks for the book.[71]

Even the primary distributor for this book became painfully uneasy about his circumcised state on reading a draft of the text. It's not comfortable knowing that what I write will make others start to feel anew a violation they've long ago suppressed, to begin to comprehend a loss they've been unaware of. It's a responsibility I don't take lightly. Part of me would much rather let sleeping dogs lie—"It's too late for me, why bother dealing with it?" But another part of me isn't satisfied with that, doesn't want to live in denial and to pass on lies and mutilations. I don't know of any other way to bring about personal and social healing than for those of us who've been violated to get through our denial of our violation, to mourn our loss, to accept it, and to resolve that we shall pass a better way on to our children.

HEARTS AND MINDS—VISION OF AN INTACT WORLD

I arrived one day at the office of the National Organization of Circumcision Information Resource Centers (NOCIRC) to find its director weeping at her phone. She had just retrieved messages from her answering machine. A brand-new father had called twice while she was out, saying that he and his wife had considered the pros and cons, including a piece of NOCIRC literature they'd somehow come across, and had decided to circumcise. The deciding factor, he said, was that the NOCIRC brochure was "emotional," and so his infant son was set to become, thirty minutes after the last call and in the father's words, "civilized."

We suffer from a tyranny of the intellect over the emotions. A dictatorship of the head over the heart instead of an integration of these complementary aspects of our being. Tradition dictating to, not being informed by, protective and nurturing instinct. A separation of ourselves from nature, from nonhuman animals, from "uncivilized" peoples. This seems to me a fundamental "dis-ease" at the root of many of our problems—from widespread genital mutilation to class exploitation, sexual violence, and Armageddon overkill in disguise as national defense.

Like so many of the crucial issues we face today, circumcision is highly emotional as well as requiring clear-headed thinking and analysis. We need to bring all that our heads and our hearts have to offer in order to transform our pain and our loss into action for an intact world; each of us brings a different perspective and different talents to this movement. Since there are songs about everything else under the sun, we can even sing about circumcision, too! Recording artist Geoff Morgan performed a humorous song about it at a national men's gathering that I attended,[72] while another singer and songwriter expresses his feelings this way:

> Every time that I go to the bathroom to take a pee
> I'm holding the evidence of what they did to me
> They butchered my penis and frankly just between us
> It makes me kind of sad to see
> That my foreskin's gone, I'm not the man I used to be
>
> Violence and sex, they seem to go hand in hand
> Why that is I think I'm finally starting to understand...
>
> ....If I ever have a boy I tell you what I'm going to do
>
> I'll say, "Son, we look a little different, you and I
> You've got an extra piece of flesh, let me tell you why
> We left your body intact and that's a natural fact
> We didn't want to see you cry..."

—"For My Foreskin," song copyright © 1989 by Jess Grant[73]

KEENING AND A DREAM REMEMBERED

My 43rd birthday finds me at an all-day dance workshop in an old former church in north London. At one point toward the end of the day all 40-odd of us participants are gathered in a large circle on the floor, dwarfed by the hall's vaulting ceiling of massive timbers. Someone starts humming in a deep voice, and soon everybody's doing it. The person next to me motions for us to put our backs together. This faces me to the woman on my other side, and eventually everybody in the circle is arranged in pairs. The different voices, the soundings (no words), become increasingly varied. Mine and my partner's become wailings of unspoken hurts from deep within our breasts. For me, the hurt is circumcision, mutilation, deprivation of part of my sexuality.

A week before, an English friend had told me how she'd been disappointed that the last several of her lovers were circumcised. (In England, circumcision is now uncommon, and most people are astounded that it's still practiced in the States.) Then I had a dream. Someone I had recently been lusting over was examining my penis, focusing on a clitoris-like protrusion from the underside of the glans where the frenulum is. Since it had been cut off or mutilated, she lost sexual interest. I didn't make the grade. This related to my recent realization that, without a foreskin, my penis is less fun both to play with and to *be* played with.

Now, as I voice my loss in the workshop, I understand: words are so inadequate to express what many of us have to express about our various hurts and violations. To use words and normal speech, no matter how eloquently, is to betray the depth of our feelings, to betray feelings which don't fit into the niceties of conventional speech. We need something deeper. Traditionally, in a variety of social movements, civil disobedience has come from this realization about the inadequacies of speech alone. As Thoreau put it, civil disobedience is voting with one's whole body, not a slip of paper only.

I don't know much about keening, but that's what we were doing, what I was doing, there in that old London church. I know that keening is used by some feminists as a resurrection of an ancient way for women to mourn and wail their deepest sorrows at their lot in life. There could be no more appropriate form of voicing our feelings about what's been done to us. Perhaps through hearing keening, those who cannot think or feel beyond the latest medical justification for circumcision would have their hearts opened at last.

THE JOURNEY BEGUN

I've only begun my own process of getting in touch with the long-suppressed, long-denied trauma, the grief, the loss that so many men have experienced. With an understanding lover, I've cried over my loss but, like many others with this suppressed terror, I still can't bring myself to watch a video of a circumcision from beginning to end. The pain is simply too great. I've been trying foreskin restoration through sustained gentle stretching of what's left. Though I've not been doing it for a very long time (and not always consistently), I'm surprised at the positive psychological effect I've experienced from my penis starting to look, to feel, to be whole again.

In addition to the personal benefit, as more and more of us strive to get back as much as we can of what we've lost, we create a statement against mutilation more powerful than the most eloquent speech. I'm interested in but wary of surgical techniques; though some insurance companies will pay for the procedure, I have little trust in the profession that cut it off to put it back. I speak openly about the issue with friends and colleagues, and find sympathetic understanding, positive support, and appreciation as frequently as laughter, joking, aversion, and retreat into tradition—which after all are only ways of initially dealing with uncomfortable new information. I enjoy the much-needed lightness that humor brings to the subject. I'm writing, facilitating workshops, and helping organize political action against routine circumcision. I dream of ten thousand men all across the country, joined by other mutilated men and women all over the world, no longer silent, keening our loss to those who continue to cut off parts of babies' genitals, placing our bodies between the circumcisers and their intended victims, demanding that the violence stop with us, declaring that the healing shall now begin.

One foot in front of the other, this unexpected journey has begun. I don't know where it will lead. I only know I have to go.

Ω

AFTERWORD

MANY OF US HAVE BEEN CIRCUMCISED because our parents thought it was best for us. We've had our sons circumcised for the same reason, and because we didn't understand the risks. We didn't know about the loss of sexual feeling. We didn't realize that medical reasons for circumcision are only attempts to justify a very ancient practice that has outlived whatever useful purpose it may once have had.

Now that we know better, we can begin to allow our children their full biological heritage. We can give them a chalice instead of the blade.

A friend used to take long winter trips to Mexico for his health. In the midst of feeling overwhelmed by the sorting, packing, and planning necessary before each trip, he would get to a point where he'd simply lock up and go. "If the Captain waited 'til everything was all shipshape before setting sail," he'd say, "the ship would never leave port."

I feel a bit that way about this book. I want to learn more, and I want to find better ways to write and organize what I have to say. In short, I'm still grappling with this issue and how to present it...and with my own loss as a circumcised man. Of course, there is no end, really, but the time has come to put this book into the world—into your hands, your head, and your heart—with all its imperfections. If I have offended, whether unnecessarily or by speaking a painful truth, I ask that you let me know. If I have said anything that you feel is unfairly exaggerated, not true, or taken out of context, I ask that you correct me. If you have ideas of how this book can be made better or if you have additional information or a personal experience that might be useful to me in preparing the next edition, please write. I will not identify you in print unless you give me permission.

And if this book speaks to you in some special way, I'd like to know that, too. You can write me c/o C. Olson, P.O. Box 5100-CB, Santa Cruz, CA 95063-5100.

Ω

ENDNOTES

(with this book's page numbers in parentheses)

1 (11) On masthead of *The Victims Speak*, newsletter (no longer published) of The Victims Speak, from unpublished 1989 book manuscript by Marilyn Fayre Milos, R.N., Director, National Organization of Circumcision Information Resource Centers.

2 (15) King, Lowell R., M.D., "The Pros and Cons of Neonatal Circumcision" (unpublished), cited by Romberg, Rosemary, *Circumcision: The Painful Dilemma*, 1985, Bergin & Garvey, South Hadley, MA, p. 274.

3 (15) Stagg, Del, P.D., "A Basis for Decision on Circumcision," from *Compulsory Hospitalization or Freedom of Choice in Childbirth?*, Vol. III (Transcripts of the 1978 NAPSAC Convention—Stewart & Stewart) Ch. 63, p. 833, cited by Romberg, Rosemary, *Circumcision: The Painful Dilemma*, p. 257.

4 (15) "The Prepuce: A Mistake of Nature?" by Drs. Jan Winberg, Ingela Bollgren, Leif Gothefors, Maria Herthelius, and Kjell Tullus, *The Lancet*, 18 March 1989.

5 (17) "UTI Studies Refuted," *NOCIRC Newsletter*, National Organization of Circumcision Information Resource Centers, Vol. 4, No. 1, Winter 1989–90, p. 2.

6 (17) Marino, Leonard J., M.D., "An emphatic vote against circumcision," letter to *Contemporary Pediatrics*, Nov. 1989, pp. 11, 14.

7 (17) Romberg, Rosemary, personal correspondence with author, Jan. 1990.

8 (18) Gellis, Sydney, *American Journal of Diseases of Childhood*, Vol. 132, Dec. 1978, p. 1168, cited in Romberg, Rosemary, *Circumcision: The Painful Dilemma*, p. 247.

9 (18) Romberg, Rosemary, *Circumcision: The Painful Dilemma*, 1985, Bergin & Garvey, South Hadley, MA, p. 246.

10 (19) Fleis, Paul, M.D., "Care of the Intact Penis," NOCIRC Newsletter, Vol. 4, No. 1, Winter 1989–90, p 2.

11 (21) Desantis, George, "Circumcision: Prime Cut," *QQ Magazine* (no longer published), March/April 1976, cited by John Erickson, Gulf Coast Infant Circumcision Information Center (NOCIRC affiliate), May 1987 mailing.

12 (21) "Circumcision Ban," *NOCIRC Newsletter*, Vol. 4, No. 1, Winter 1989–90, p. 2.

13 (22) "Canadian Paediatric Society Upholds Anti-circumcision Stand," *NOCIRC Newsletter*, Vol. 4, No. 1, Winter 1989–90, p. 2.

14 (22) Romberg, p. 248.

15 (24) Letter received by The Victims Speak, dated 19 Oct. 1988.

16 (25) Romberg, Rosemary, correspondence with the author, Jan. 1990.

17 (25) Trager, James, Medical Tribune, 8 June 1989, cited by *NOCIRC Newsletter*, Vol. 4., No. 1, Winter 1989–90, "Media Distorts AAP Report," p. 1.

18 (25) Collected by the National Organization of Circumcision Information Resource Centers.

19 (26) Brower, Vicki, "Circumcision's comeback?", Family Report, *American Health*, Sep. 1989, p. 126.

20 (27) "AAP Alters Position and Confuses Parents," *NOCIRC Newsletter*, Vol. 4, No. 1, Winter 1989–90, p. 1.

21 (29) Romberg, p. 3.

22 (29) Bryk, Felix, *Sex and Circumcision: A Study of Phallic Worship and Mutilation in Men and Women*, Brandon House, North Hollywood, California, 1967, p. 80, cited by Romberg, p. 3.

23 (30) Daly, Mary, *Gyn Ecology: The Metaphysics of Radical Feminism*, The Sacred Passage, Ch. 5, "African Genital Mutilation: The Unspeakable Atrocities," p. 165. Her reference: Henny Harald Hansen, "Clitoridectomy: Female Circumcision in Egypt," *Folk*, Vol. 14–15 (1972/73), p. 18.

24 (30) Information on response to female circumcision in Britain, Italy, and France from a conversation (1989) between the author and Marilyn Fayre Milos, Director, National Organization of Circumcision Information Resource Centers, based on a telephone conversation between her and Fran Hosken, Women's International Network.

25 (31) Dr. Snyder spoke at the First International Symposium on Circumcision, 1–3 March 1989, Anaheim, California. The author was in attendance.

26 (32) Fink, Aaron J., M.D., *Circumcision: A Parent's Decision for Life*, Kavanah Publishing, 1988.

27 (32) Ibid., p. 12.

28 (32) Ibid., p. 17.

29 (33) "Washington State Saves Health-care Dollars," NOCIRC Newsletter, Vol. 4, No. 1, Winter 1989–90, p. 2.

30 (33) Original citation lost. Referred to in "Circumcision's comeback?", Family Report by Vicki Brower, *American Health*, Sep. 1989, p. 126, in which Ms. Bower implies that the AAP "recommends" that parents take these factors into account, not that they simply *observe* that they do.

31 (34) Letter reprinted in *NOCIRC Newsletter, circa 1988.*

32 (35) Fink, p. 1.

33 (36) "Working Together for Children's Rights," May 1989, International Save the Children Alliance, 147 rue de Lauzanne, CH-1202 Geneva, Switzerland, p. 2, "Basic Principles."

34 (36) "High Court Awards Scarred Child £10,000," *NOCIRC Newsletter*, Vol. 4, No. 1, Winter 1989–90.

35 (38) "The First Cut," Parenting magazine, 501 Second St., San Francisco, CA 94107, June/July 1989, p. 56.

36 (40) Kitihara, Michio, Fil. Dr., "A Cross-cultural Test of the Freudian Theory of Circumcision," *International Journal of Psychoanalytic Psychotherapy*, Vol. 5, 1976, p. 541, cited by Romberg, p. 10.

37 (41) Frederick and Jeannine Parvati Baker, 960 S. Ross Lane, Joseph, UT 84739.

38 (41) Ya'acov Khan, 5 Bittaford Terrace, Bittaford, South Devon PL21 ODX, England.

39 (43) Anonymity requested.

40 (46) Wrana, Phoebe, *Historical Review*, "Circumcision" p. 387, cited by Romberg, p. 88.

41 (46) From materials sent out by the Alternative Bris Support Group, 1989.

42 (47) Edward Wallerstein, "Circumcision and Anti-Semitism: An Update," *Humanistic Judaism* (undated photocopy).

43 (47) Romberg, p. 10, re: tribal societies in Australia and New Guinea.

44 (48) Bettelheim, Bruno, *Symbolic Wounds: Puberty Rites and the Envious Male*, Thames and Hudson, London, 1955. Out of print. (Available through inter-library loan.)

45 (49) Radio interview with Ricky Sherover Marcuse broadcast on KPFA, Berkeley, California, circa 1988, taped by author.

46 (50) "The Slaughterer," *Isaac Bashevis Singer: The Collected Stories*, 1982, Farrar, Straus & Giroux, 19 Union Square West, New York, NY 10003. $12.95 paper, $19.95 hard cover.

47 (51) Zalman Schachter-Shalomi, "How To Deal With A Jewish Issue: Circumcision," *A Mensch Among Men: Explorations in Jewish Masculinity*, anthology, Harry Brod, editor. p. 83. The Crossing Press, Freedom, CA 95019. $10.95 paper. Originally from "The First Step," copyright © Zalman Schachter-Shalomi and Donald Gropman.

48 (52) Cited in *Jewish Vegetarians* (undated), newsletter of the Jewish Vegetarian Society, P.O. Box 1463, Baltimore, MD 21203.

49 (52) Phone conversation with the author, mid-October 1988.

50 (55) Rabbi Burt Jacobson (Jewish Renewal Movement), Kehilla Synagogue, Oakland/ Berkeley, California. Interview with the author, June 1989.

51 (58) First International Symposium on Circumcision, 1–3 March 1989, Anaheim, California. The author was in attendance.

52 (58) Briggs, Anne, *Circumcision: What Every Parent Should Know*, p. 172.

53 (58) Flyer received in the mail by the author in 1989 from a circumcisionist, as evidence that the preservationist movement was racist.

54 (61) Written statement received by The Victims Speak, undated, summer 1988.

55 (62) Daly, Mary, *Gyn Ecology: The Metaphysics of Radical Feminism*, Ch. 4, "Chinese Footbinding: On Footnoting the Three-Inch 'Lotus Hooks'," pp. 134–152, cited by Romberg, p.56.

56 (62) Schechet, Jacob, Rabbi & Mohel, *The Layman's Guide to the Covenant of Circumcision*, p. 16, cited by Romberg, p. 56.

57 (62) From literature sent out by the Alternative Bris Support Group, 1989.

58 (62) Interview by author with Rabbi Burt Jacobson (Jewish Renewal Movement), Kehilla Synagogue, Oakland/Berkeley, California, June 1989.

59 (63) Romberg, p. 55.

60 (65) Karsenty, Nelly, "A Mother Questions *Brit Milla*," *Humanistic Judaism*, Summer 1988, p. 14.

61 (65) "Jewish Feminists Prompt Protests at Wailing Wall" (with photo), *New York Times*, 2 Dec. 1988, p. A10, quoting Rabbi Meir Yehuda Getz (Orthodox).

62 (67) Letter received by the National Organization of Circumcision Information Resource Centers.

63 (68) Undated and uncredited newspaper clipping received in the mail by the author on 26 Feb. 1990, from a medical advice column by "Dr. Lamb," Copyright 1985 News American Syndicate.

64 (69) Abbott, Franklin, "What To Do When Shit Happens: Reaction and Responsibility," Health and Healing section, *Southern Voice*,1989 (undated photocopy).

65 (69) From information in *The Human Connection* by Ashley Montague and Floyd Matson, cited in unpublished 1989 book manuscript on circumcision by Marilyn Fayre Milos, R.N., Director, National Organization of Circumcision Information Resource Centers.

66 (72) Letter received January 1989 by the National Organization of Circumcision Information Resource Centers.

67 (72) "Statement of Principles and Purpose," The Victims Speak, undated, circa 1988.

68 (73) From the introductory talk at which Marilyn Milos was presented the Maurine Ricke Award for Clinical Excellence in Perinatal Nursing, California Nurses' Association, Region 9, April 1988.

69 (74) Badawi, Mohammed, M.D., M.P.H. First International Symposium on Circumcision, 1–3 March 1989, Anaheim, California. The author was in attendance.

70 (75) Cited, unreferenced, in an issue of *The Vegan* magazine (UK).

71 (77) Letter received by the author December 1989.

72 (78) National Organization of Changing Men (NOCM), Seattle, summer 1988

73 (78) Jess Grant, San Francisco, c/o The Victims Speak, P.O. Box 5100, Santa Cruz, CA 95063-5100.

DataBank
(Appendices)

Note:

The Second International Symposium on Circumcision
will be held sometime in May 1991 in San Francisco
to present research findings and
"organize national and international task force committees
to establish guidelines for eliminating the practice of genital mutilation of
infants and children.
Continuing education credit will be provided."

Contact NOCIRC, Appendix A, below.

Appendix A—
Resources for Information and Action

Organizations:

All these organizations operate with volunteer labor on a shoestring budget. Donations accompanying requests are most appreciated; please be generous.

National Organization of Circumcision Information Resource Centers (NOCIRC), P.O. Box 2512, San Anselmo, CA 94960, TEL: 415-488-9883. Marilyn Fayre Milos, R.N., Director. Clearinghouse for regional centers and contacts nationwide and in Australia, Canada, England, France, New Zealand, and South Africa. Send SASE with 2 ounces postage plus at least $3 for a general information packet (a larger donation will be used to further the cause) and receipt of newsletter. Videos, legal information, brochures (general and on foreskin restoration), hot line, catalog, latest medical and legal information.

Alternative Bris Support Group, c/o Natali Bivas, 248 Ventura Avenue, Palo Alto, CA 94306, TEL: 415-424-9855. For Jewish parents considering bris (brit) without circumcision.

Peaceful Beginnings. Rosemary Romberg, 13020 Homestead Ct., Anchorage, AK 99516. TEL: 907-345-4813. Much original material not available elsewhere, including on circumcision and Christianity. Catalog.

The Victims Speak, c/o P.O. Box 5100, Santa Cruz, CA 95063-5100. Men, friends, and loved ones victimized by circumcision in various ways and degrees organizing nonviolent action to raise public awareness and end genital mutilation. SASE, one ounce. For those ready to act or support action or wishing to organize or host workshops; general information inquiries not answered. For general information, write NOCIRC, above.

Women's International Network (WIN), 187 Grant Street, Lexington, MA 02173. Source of information on female circumcision around the world. Publishes *WIN News*, Fran Hosken, Editor.

Brothers United for Future Foreskins (BUFF), Box 26377, Tempe, AZ 85285-6377. Information on foreskin restoration through stretching techniques.

Foreskin Restoration Support Group, TEL: 415-826-5972 or 415-827-4077. Moral support and practical advice for gay and straight, cut and uncut men interested in stretching techniques. This San Francisco Bay Area group can also offer advice on how set up such a group in your area.

Further Reading / Books:

Circumcision: An American Health Fallacy, by Edward Wallerstein. 1980. Springer Publishing Co., 536 Broadway, New York, NY 10012.

Circumcision: The Painful Dilemma, by Rosemary Romberg. 1985. Bergen & Garvey, 88 Post Road West, Box 5007, Westport, CT 06881. Perhaps the most comprehensive book on the medical, historical, and cultural aspects of genital mutilations. Out of print. Check inter-library loan program of local library. (Letters to the publisher to encourage reprinting would also be appreciated.)

Circumcision: What Every Parent Should Know, by Anne Briggs. 1985. Birth and Parenting Publications, P.O. Box 286, Earlysville, VA 22936. TEL: 804-977-1529.

Foreskin Restoration (Uncircumcision), by Mark Waring. Stretching techniques, anti-surgical bias. Staple bound, $14.95. Brothers United for Future Foreskins (BUFF), P.O. Box 1501, Metairie, LA 70004-1501. Out of print. Contact Arizona BUFF (Organizations, above).

The Hidden Face of Eve: Women in the Arab World, by Nawal el Saadawi, M.D., former director of education in the Egyptian Ministry of Health, former editor of *Health* magazine, and author of *Women and Sex*. Beacon Press, 25 Beacon Street, Boston, MA 02108.

The Politics of Reproductive Ritual, by K.E. and J.M. Paige. 1981. University of California Press, Berkeley.

Prisoners of Ritual: An Odyssey into Female Genital Circumcision in Africa, by Hanny Lightfoot-Klein. 1989. Haworth Press, 12 West 32nd St., New York, NY 10001-3813 or 10 Alice St., Binghampton, NY 13904-1580.

Symbolic Wounds: Puberty Rites and the Envious Male, by Bruno Bettelheim. 1955. Thames and Hudson, London. Out of print.

Further Reading / Pamphlets, Magazines, etc.

The Circumcision Decision, by Edward Wallerstein. 1980. Pennypress, 1100 23rd Ave., Seattle, WA 98112.

Circumcision: Information, Misinformation, Disinformation, by Edward Wallerstein. 1986. $2.50 from NOCIRC, P.O. Box 2512, San Anselmo, CA 94960.

Circumcision: Mothering Special Edition. A magazine-format collection of articles, letters and resources from Mothering Magazine 1976-1988. $7.00 + .50 postage. Mothering Magazine, P.O. Box 1690, Santa Fe, NM 87504. TEL: 505-984-8116.

Circumcision: The Uniquely American Medical Enigma, by Edward Wallerstein. 1986. Pennypress, 1100 23rd Avenue, Seattle, WA 98112.

Good News for Boys, P.O. Box 584, Tacoma, WA 98401. J.C. Jensen, editor. For boys who are intact.

Humanistic Judaism, quarterly, Summer 1988 (Vol. XVI, No. III), articles on theme of "Becoming Parents" dealing with circumcision from a non-dogmatic religious and cultural perspective. Single back issue $4.00 plus $1 postage, or $15/year from Society for Humanistic Judaism, 28611 West Twelve Mile Road, Farmington Hills, MI 48018, TEL: 313-478-7610.

Making America Safe for Foreskins: Letters Published and Unpublished, by John A. Erickson. $3 postpaid from John A. Erickson, 1096 Beach Blvd., Biloxi, MS 39530. A selection of letters to editors, etc., by a prolific preservationist. "I waited for years for someone to say what I thought should be said. But no one did. So I started saying it myself."

Saturday Evening Post, Dec. 1981. Two articles, color photographs. Libraries.

The Truth Seeker magazine, July/August 1989 issue, "Crimes of Genital Mutilation," $4 + $1 postage and handling from NOCIRC or from *The Truth Seeker*, P.O. Box 2832, San Diego, CA 92112-2832.

When Your Baby Boy is Not Circumcised, by Edward Wallerstein. 1982. Pennypress, 1100 23rd Avenue, Seattle, WA 98112.

1990 Guide for Anticircumcision Activists, SASE and $3.00 to NOCIRC of New Jersey, P.O. Box 562, Lakehurst, NJ 08733-0562.

Video & Audio Tapes (video unless otherwise noted)

A Matter of Choice, Orion Express, 39 Marie St., Sausalito, CA 94965.

Newborn Circumcision, Foresight Productions, 1302 Oakland Ave., Durham, NC 27705.

NOCIRC Conference Tape, NOCIRC, P.O. Box 2512, San Anselmo, CA 94960.

The Circumcision Question, Perennial Education, Inc., 930 Pitner, Evanston, IL 60202.

The First International Symposium on Circumcision (audio), Master Duplicators, 11042 Bettes Place, Garden Grove, CA 92640.

The First International Symposium on Circumcision, Promo Video, 2240 Morley St., #7, San Diego, CA 92111.

St. Catherine's Wedding Ring, University of Southern California School of Cinema-Television, Film Distribution Center, University Park, Los Angeles, CA 90089-2211, Attn: Dave Edelson/Debra Kahn.

Appendix B—Getting It Back: Foreskin Restoration

There are two ways to re-cover the glans bared by circumcision: stretching what's left and surgery. Stretching is slower, safer, and cheaper. Surgery is quicker, riskier (a lot depends on the doctor), and expensive (though insurance companies sometimes pay).

Stretching

This is a beginning method of foreskin stretching/restoration for those with "tight" circumcisions, with little or no foreskin left. It is based on my own personal experience, adapted from information from NOCIRC and *Foreskin Restoration (Uncircumcision)* (Appendix A). There is a limit to how much stretching can be done with this technique, so after several months (or from the beginning for those with whom the circumciser was a little more generous), men usually switch to other methods: tape ring, silicon cone, etc. Contact NOCIRC or BUFF for details.

This description should not be taken for medical advice—or advice of any kind, for that matter. What works for me (or for whoever writes about the subject) may or may not work for you. Read up, experiment, adapt, use common sense, and err on the side of caution. And be sure to report your progress and any innovations to NOCIRC.

◊ Purchase a roll of 1"-wide tape (paper, nylon, rayon, or other) from a pharmacy.

◊ Cut off a 3" or 4" strip and a shorter piece about 1" or 1 1/2" long.

◊ Align the shorter piece parallel to and in the middle of the longer one, pressing the sticky sides together, leaving the longer piece with two uncovered sticky ends and a covered unsticky center (somewhat like a bandaid).

◊ Cut a hole ("pee hole") in the now non-sticky center section.

◊ With your penis in the flaccid (soft) state—preferably after a bath or shower when the skin is warm and more pliable—gently stretch your remaining foreskin (or shaft skin, if you have no foreskin left) as far over the glans as comfortably possible and tape it in place. Taping can be done top to bottom or left to right—or, using two of these tape devices, both directions, crossing the two. The pee hole(s) should be over the urinary opening to allow urination. The sticky ends of the tape device should touch only the foreskin/shaft skin, not the glans.

◊ Let comfort, patience, and safety be your guides.

5-yard rolls of tape sell for about $3.00. I prefer paper tape, which is easier to remove, an advantage especially if the bandage slips and sticks to the glans! Unfortunately, it also slips and comes loose easier. Nylon, rayon, and other tapes are also available, and they stick better. (If you use a high-stick tape that gets stuck to the glans, don't panic—normal sweating will usually be sufficient to loosen it. If you're impatient, acetone will help, but care should be taken to avoid getting it in the urinary tract opening.) Nocturnal erections aid in the stretching process, but if they cause discomfort, the tape can be removed at night.

According to men who've done it, pubic hair that is pulled up the shaft recedes as the shaft skin gradually stretches, and it takes two, three, or four years of fairly consistent stretching before a full foreskin is obtained.

Several other kinds of stretching devices have been invented by imaginative men. If you want to experiment, *be careful*—stretching should *always be gentle and never hurt or impede the flow of blood in either flaccid or erect state, awake or asleep.* If you can find a good doctor who is sympathetic to your attempts (ask around—it won't be easy), he or she could give additional suggestions.

Surgery

The following physicians are listed by NOCIRC as performing surgical foreskin restoration. They can be contacted for further information.

Dr. Charles Horton, Hague Medical Center, 400 West Brambleton, Norfolk, VA 23510, TEL: 216-292-2923

Dr. Sheldon Artz, 3755 Orange Place, Beachwood, OH 44122, TEL: 216-292-2923.

Dr. Milton Edgerton, Box 376, University of Virginia Medical Center, Charlottesville, VA 22908, TEL: 804-924-5068.

Before making any decision for surgical restoration, it is essential to do a lot of research, and to talk to the prospective surgeon's former restoration patients. Two men are listed by NOCIRC as having undergone foreskin restoration and being willing to talk about it. I've met the first, who has written about his experience and appeared on national television.

Richard Steiner, P.O. Box 63992, Pheonix, AZ 85082, TEL: 602-840-8019

John Strand, 3431 Starbend, San Antonio, TX 78217, TEL: 512-655-8251

Appendix C—Female Circumcision: A Victim's Account

The following is Nawal el Saadawi, M.D.'s account of her circumcision, age 8. From her book *The Hidden Face of Eve: Women in the Arab World.* Dr. Saadawi was fired as director of education in the Egyptian Ministry of Health and editor of *Health* magazine for publishing the book *Women and Sex* in that sexually repressed society. For further information on female circumcision, contact Women's International Network (Appendix A—Organizations).

"I was six years old that night when I lay in my bed, warm and peaceful in the pleasurable state which lies halfway between wakefulness and sleep. I felt something like a huge hand, cold and rough, fumbling over my body, as though looking for something. Almost simultaneously another hand, as cold and as rough and as big as the first one, was clapped over my mouth, to prevent me from screaming.

"They carried me to the bathroom. I do not know how many of them there were, nor do I remember their faces, or whether they were women or men. The world seemed enveloped in a dark fog; perhaps they put some kind of a cover over my eyes. All I remember is that I was frightened and that there were many of them, and that something like an iron grasp caught hold of my hand, and my arms, and my thighs, so that I became unable to resist or even to move. I also remember the icy touch of the bathroom tiles under my naked body and unknown voices and humming sounds interrupted now and again by a rasping metallic sound which reminded me of the butcher when he used to sharpen his knife before slaughtering a sheep...

"My blood was frozen in my veins. I thought thieves had broken into my room and kidnapped me from my bed. I was afraid they were getting ready to cut my throat, which was what always happened with disobedient girls in the stories my old rural grandmother told.

"I strained my ears trying to catch the metallic, rasping sound. The moment it ceased, I felt as though my heart had stopped beating, too. I was unable to see, and somehow my breathing seemed to have stopped. Yet I imagined the rasping sound coming closer and closer to me. Somehow it was not approaching my neck as I had expected, but another part of my body, somewhere below my belly, as though seeking something buried between my thighs. At that very moment, I realized that my thighs had been pulled wide apart, and that each of my legs was being held as far away from the other as possible, as though gripped by steel fingers that never relinquished their pressure. Then suddenly the sharp metallic edge dropped between my thighs and cut off a piece of flesh from my body. I screamed with pain despite the tight hand held over my mouth. The pain was like a searing flare that went through my whole body. After a few moments, I saw a red pool of blood around my hips.

"I did not know what they had cut off, and I did not try to find out. I just wept, and called out to my mother for help. But the worst shock of all was when I looked around and found her standing by my side. Yes, it was she. In flesh and blood, right in the midst of these strangers, she was talking to them, and smiling at them, as though they had not just participated in slaughtering her daughter."

Appendix D—Male Circumcision: An Eye-witness Account

The following is an account of a then-student nurse of the first circumcision she witnessed. Reprinted by permission of Marilyn Fayre Milos, R.N. Copyright © 1989 Marilyn Fayre Milos.

"We students filed into the newborn nursery to find a baby strapped spread-eagle to a plastic board on a counter top across the room. He was struggling against his restraints—tugging, whimpering, and then crying helplessly. No one was tending the infant, but when I asked my instructor if I could comfort him, she said, 'Wait til the doctor gets here.' I wondered how a teacher of the healing arts could watch someone suffer and not offer assistance. I wondered about the doctor's power which could intimidate others from following protective instincts. When he did arrive, I immediately asked the doctor if I could help the baby. He told me to put my finger into the baby's mouth; I did, and the baby sucked. I stroked his little head and spoke softly to him. He began to relax, and was momentarily quiet.

"The silence was soon broken by a piercing scream—the baby's reaction to having his foreskin pinched and crushed as the doctor attached the clamp to his penis. The shriek intensified when the doctor inserted an instrument between the foreskin and the glans (head of the penis), tearing the two structures apart. (They are normally attached to each other during infancy so the foreskin can protect the sensitive glans from urine and feces.) The baby started shaking his head back and forth—the only part of his body free to move—as the doctor used another clamp to crush the foreskin length-wise, where he then cut. This made the opening of the foreskin large enough to insert a circumcision instrument, the device used to protect the glans from being severed during the surgery.

"The baby began to gasp and choke, breathless from his shrill, continuous screams. How could anyone say circumcision is painless when the suffering is so obvious? My bottom lip began to quiver, tears filled my eyes and spilled over, I found my own sobs difficult to contain. How much longer could this go on?

"During the next stage of the surgery, the doctor crushed the foreskin against the circumcision instrument and then, finally, amputated it. The baby was limp, exhausted, spent.

"I had not been prepared, nothing could have prepared me, for this experience. To see a part of this baby's penis being cut off—without an anesthetic—was devastating. But even more shocking was the doctor's comment, barely audible several octaves below the piercing screams of the baby: 'There's no medical reason for doing this.' I couldn't believe my ears, my knees became weak, and I felt sick to my stomach. I couldn't believe that medical professionals, dedicated to helping and healing, could inflict such unnecessary pain and anguish on innocent babies."

Appendix E—The Victims Speak

Considering the impact that circumcision has on men, it's no wonder that some become "foreskin fanatics" or "foreskin fundamentalists," as circumcisionists refer to those who value highly that which has so violently been taken away from them or from those they love.

The voices of circumcision victims—of those who *know* they're victims and are willing to say so—are conspicuously absent from the circumcision debate. They give the lie to the claim that "the baby gets over it." It is possible, of course, to write off such complaints as symptoms of psychological problems lying elsewhere, just as it is possible to write off the psychological dislocations caused by racism, sexism, and poverty as purely personal phenomena.

Considering that most circumcised men are denied information about the effects of circumcision, considering that most of us never allow our feelings about our circumcised state to surface in our adult lives, and considering that there is such strong tradition and social validation for circumcision, it's quite remarkable that there are any voices of protest at all. The medical and scientific community have not considered the psychological impact of genital mutilation to be an issue important enough to study, so mostly what we have is a disturbing number of reports from individual victims.

The following quotes are from circumcised men. They were compiled by Rosemary Romberg of Peaceful Beginnings and by John Erickson and Jeffrey R. Wood of the Gulf Coast Infant Circumcision Information Center, contactable via NOCIRC (Appendix A). While some at first reading may seem ridiculous (most of us are not used to taking circumcision seriously), don't be surprised if what happened to me happens to you—one or more of the comments may express some unconsious feeling you have, with the result that the quote will stick in your mind like a catchy tune from the radio.

Quotes

"I've wondered all my life how it feels to have a foreskin."

"There's a story by Harlan Ellison with a title that exactly conveys my feelings about having been circumcised as a baby. It's 'I have no mouth and I must scream.'"

"I think of myself and other circumcised men as amputees."

"I am always thinking: where is my foreskin?"

"I think of myself as existing in two pieces: my missing foreskin and the rest of me."

"Circumcision is partial castration!"

"I feel like half a man."

"Being circumcised just isn't me."

"I have always felt I was cut off from my foreskin, not vice versa."

"If you think the only *un*circumcised man in a shower feels different, imagine how the only *circumcised* man feels."

"I have revenge fantasies about circumcision."

"I have had a lifelong hangup about foreskins because I never had one. I am heterosexual except for my interest in the foreskins of other men."

"I think I could have accepted a deformity that was an accident of nature, but I can't accept that someone did this to me."

"I have resented my circumcision ever since I saw my first uncircumcised friend when I was five or six."

"What circumcision did to my body is bad enough, but what it did to my head is worse."

"Whenever I take a shower I always retract my imaginary foreskin and wash under it, just as if I had never been circumcised."

"My feelings about the doctor who circumcised me are too violent to describe."

"I have nightmares about being circumcised by force."

"I tried several times to ask my mother about what had been done to me; but when I opened my mouth to speak, the words stuck in my throat and no sound came out."

"Why would anyone cut up a baby's penis? How could anyone allow himself or someone else to do it."

"I couldn't even make myself say 'circumcised' until I was in my twenties."

"I never told my parents how I feel."

"I was just a baby—I couldn't stop them."

"I pretended I didn't care."

"I envy my dog."

"The fact that other boys were circumcised too never made me feel any better."

"My mother told me she could hear my screams from the other end of the hall."

"There's something very, very wrong and very frightening about a society that systematically tortures and mutilates babies."

"My greatest fear to this day is having a knife pulled on me."

"I have never been able to accept the fact that when I was a baby someone cut part of my penis off. Sometimes I think I'm beginning to make some sort of adjustment to it, but then I see an unmutilated man in a shower or magazine and I become overwhelmed by uncontrollable feelings of outrage and disbelief that I was made the victim for life of something so sick."

"Adrenalin shoots through me when I hear the word 'circumcised'—I freeze."

"When I was a child, I prayed I would get my foreskin back in Heaven."

"I am Jewish and I hate the tradition that robbed me of my best part."

"Imagine how the Elephant Man would have felt if he had found out that he had been born normal but that someone had done that to him. That's how I feel."

"What possible advantage could there be to removing from the penis its only movable part?"

"I wanted to be a girl when I was a child because I knew that girls weren't circumcised."

"I used to think there were two kinds of boys: circumcised boys like me and real boys."

"I went to a nude beach in Yugoslavia and felt like a freak."

"I was circumcised when I was five—seventy years ago. I felt rage then and I still feel rage now."

"The worst thing about circumcision is that it produces circumcisers."

"It hurt. It bled. It left an ugly scar."

"I never got used to being circumcised. I just learned to endure it."

"I wish I could circumcise every uncircumcised man in the world, so they'd all be like me. I don't have a foreskin and no one else should have one either."

"Butchers!"

"I despise the word 'circumcised.' The sound 'cir...' makes me shudder."

"I masturbate two or three times a day, always to the same fantasy: the image of my foreskin as it would look and feel now, had it not been cut off when I was born."

"Fear, pain, crippling, disfigurement and humiliation are classic ways to break the human spirit. Circumcision includes them all."

Ω